Caring for Young Children

A *workbook for early years workers*

Jennie and Lance Lindon

Foreword by Peter Elfer

M
MACMILLAN

To Stan and Nur

First published 1994 by
THE MACMILLAN PRESS LTD
Houndmills, Basingstoke, Hampshire RG21 2XS
and London
Companies and representatives
throughout the world

ISBN 0–333–57607–1

A catalogue record for this book is available
from the British Library

Printed in Malaysia

10   9   8   7   6   5   4   3   2
02 01 00 99 98 97 96 95 94

Contents

Foreword

In the last few years major legislation has been introduced in each of the care, education and health fields. The UK has also ratified the United Nations Convention on the Rights of the Child. Legislation acts as a mirror in that it reflects changing values and beliefs in society about how adults should care for children. A good example of this is the abolition of physical punishment of children in almost all care settings outside the home.

But legislation also acts as a map, pointing to new approaches in the way we respond to children. An example is how the Children Act emphasises the need for different disciplines to work together and in partnership with parents if children's needs are really going to be understood in the round.

Of course even the most forward-looking legislation will not on its own ensure improvements in the practice of child care. Effective change requires resources, a national programme of research and development, training and, perhaps most important of all, a culture of self-appraisal within each service and within each worker. An important hallmark of a genuinely professional approach is being prepared continually to reflect on and challenge one's own practice.

The great strength of *Caring for Young Children* is that it is a workbook, to be seen as a resource and not a technical manual limited to simple instructions on how to care for young children. Readers can make a contract with themselves that to make the book effective in developing their own practice they have a part to play much beyond simply reading the words.

The readers' part is first to acknowledge and value their own experience and skills – whether new or long-established. Then they can make a commitment to use the book to support the development of their work with children. Professional supervision is key to this process, and the authors rightly refer to it from page 1.

Good luck in your study and in developing your practice. A child's greatest resource will always be the adults and other children who surround her or him. Children have an immense amount to gain from the commitment of adults to be reflective about their relationships with them.

PETER ELFER
Senior Development Officer
Early Childhood Unit
National Children's Bureau

Acknowledgements

We have learned a great deal by watching and talking with the early years workers and advisers with whom we have been in contact. We would like to thank the following people for their help and advice on early drafts of the text: Linda Williamson (Senior Health Visitor), Valerie Farebrother (Director, Division of Community and Academic Studies, West Kent College), Stuart Sillars (language consultant to the Macmillan FE care series) and Emma Lee (Consultant).

We wish to thank Boots plc for permission to use the photograph on pages 16, 32, 35, 56, 57, 58, 59, 62, 74 and 91. The remaining photographs were taken by Lance. We are grateful to the Eveline Day Nursery Schools and Rydevale Community Nursery, both in South London, for permission to take photographs.

All the examples describing children, early years workers and centres for young children are taken from the experience of real people and places. We have changed names and a few details to maintain confidentiality.

1 About this book

Caring for young children is a very important job. People who work with babies and young children need to take a very responsible attitude to their work – but it can be enjoyable as well.

Gaining experience

This book will build up your knowledge about children under 8 years old and how to take good care of them, whatever the setting in which you are training or will work in the future.

You should find that the book will develop the skills and knowledge you already have. It will help you prepare for a National or Scottish Vocational Qualification (NVQ/SVQ) in child care and education, at level 2. Appendix 1 links parts of the book with the National (Scottish) Vocational Qualifications in child care and education. The book will also support you if you are taking a BTEC, City and Guilds, RSA or NNEB course, including a General National Vocational Qualification (GNVQ) in health and social care.

Scope of the book

This book follows the NVQ/SVQ framework in covering the care and development of children up to their eighth birthday.

The tradition of distinguishing between children aged under and over 5 is based on the statutory age for starting school in the UK. Of course, the eighth birthday is no more a complete change than is the fifth. Eight-year-olds are not suddenly independent of all need for care. However, they are much more able to take care of their physical needs. Their increased self reliance and learning of important skills such as reading mean that they relate to adults in a different way from younger children. So adults – workers or parents – need to apply their caring skills in a different way.

Using the book

This book is designed to be used as a source of activities and ideas to think about. It consists of 9 chapters, each of which covers a particular area of child care and development. The chapters are divided into sections which focus on particular topics within the broad theme of the chapter.

Help from a supervisor

It is possible to use this book on your own but we hope that you will be able to turn to someone for advice and information. You may have a senior member of staff in your workplace who is responsible for supervising your work. If you are following a child care course, you will be able to consult your course tutor. We use the word 'supervisor' throughout the book to mean either of these kinds of support in your training and work.

You will find that a suggestion to ask your supervisor is part of some of the activities in this book. Your supervisor will also be the best person to help you to build up a programme of learning to ensure that you are able to link your work experience with the ideas in this book, and with your college work if you are following a course in that way. You can decide together which sections of the book you should do at a particular time and how long you should spend on them.

Your supervisor will also be able to help you arrange visits to local facilities for children, and make appointments for you to talk to other professionals.

On pages 102–3 you will find a chapter called 'Continuing to learn'. You can use the suggestions made there to monitor your learning.

Discussing and thinking

You will gain more from the book if you take opportunities to discuss the ideas given in it and any of the activities that you complete. You will be acting in a responsible manner if you ensure that you do not discuss individual children, families or colleagues outside an appropriate course or work group.

Some of the activities in this book ask you not only to *do* something, but also to *think about* what you have learned. In caring for young children it is not enough just to follow somebody else's instructions. You need to understand what you are doing and see how it relates to the children in your care.

It's equally important that you are willing to think about your own attitudes. These will show through what you do – or don't do – with the children and in your relationship with their parents. This book will help you to stand back and look carefully at the assumptions that you or other people are making. Many of the practical issues of equal opportunities arise because negative attitudes have seemed so 'normal' that they have not been questioned.

Start a work file

Your supervisor will ask you to keep a work file. Evidence of work completed may be useful to you as part of your assessment. We suggest that you start the habit of keeping notes, even if you are not following a child care course, as you read this book.

Your experience will be more useful to you later if you can refer easily to notes that you made at the time. For instance, you should write down what you learned from an activity as well as simply what you did. Your notes about a local special unit will be more useful to you in a year's time if you have written a short description of the service offered – not just the name and address of the unit.

Making responsible decisions

You will need to apply the practical suggestions in this book with due allowance for the particular setting in which you are training and for the individual children in your care.

You will find a great deal of information in the book but you may need to track down more specialised ideas. Appendix 2 and 'Further reading' at the end of the book will help you to contact useful organisations and to locate other sources of reading.

ACTIVITY

You can organise your work file now. Buy yourself a loose leaf ring binder and some coloured cardboard dividers. Label your work file by sections such as:

- activities and projects;
- local information and services;
- sources of specialised information, for example, the addresses of useful national organisations.

You will be able to reorganise a section such as activities if you then want to group them by different topics.

Key words used

People caring for children under 8 can work in a number of different settings. Instead of repeating the different possible titles for people and places each time they occur, we will use the general terms 'worker' and 'centre', as defined below.

● *Worker*

This word applies to anyone who is involved with children under 8 in any of the different possible settings. Workers may be employed or they may be offering their time on a voluntary basis.

● *Centre*

This word refers to any setting in which children are cared for as a group. Some specific points are made in the book about working as a nanny.

Two other uses of words need to be explained:

● *Parent*

We use this word to apply to any adults who have long-term responsibility for a child within their family. Some adults take this responsibility without being the biological parent.

● *He or she?*

Children and workers may be male or female. It's possible therefore for writers to get into some unhelpful repetitions of 'he or she' and 'himself or herself'. We have resolved this issue by sometimes writing in the plural about 'children' or 'workers'. We alternate between 'he' and 'she' when we give examples. You will be able to tell easily when we are making a specific point about boys or girls, men or women.

Finally

We feel sure that this book will help you in working towards good practice in caring for the under-8s, whatever the setting in which you are working. It will encourage you to feel more confident in your work, and more able to explain what you do and why.

2 Caring for young children

This chapter deals with:

- principles and legal requirements in caring for children;
- issues of good practice in any care setting.

2.1 Principles and good practice

There are several key principles that should be noticeable in the daily good practice of every care setting. Think about what this means for you.

Partnership with parents

Many centres for children now describe their work as *sharing the care* with parents. Two basic points are important wherever you are working:

1. Mutual respect
   Workers and parents need to respect one another's child care skills. You aren't doing the same job with the children as the parents are, so you don't have to feel in competition with them.
2. Communication
   You can't share the care of children unless you communicate with their parents. Communication will be most effective if you talk with and listen to each other in person and on a regular basis.

   Throughout the book you will find recommendations to consult parents and, in some circumstances, to ask their permission before doing something. Chapter 3 deals in more detail with developing positive relationships with parents.

Equal opportunities

Race, religion and culture

- Prejudice affects everybody

Around the world, children and adults experience discrimination because of prejudice. Children under 8 learn attitudes in much the same way that they learn how to count or to do up shoelaces. They listen, watch and copy.

All workers have a responsibility to show clearly through their work that they value equally all cultures and racial backgrounds. You have this responsibility whether you are working in a racially mixed city nursery or an all-white rural playgroup.

- Take positive notice of differences

You can't show a commitment to equal opportunities by ignoring the fact that children in the UK are of different skin colours and cultural backgrounds. It isn't possible to value positively something that you claim not to notice.

Black children need this active commitment from you since their sense of self worth is often under threat from prejudice – whether this is unthinking or intended to damage. However, your commitment is equally on behalf of white children – that they can have a positive identity supported by pride in their own cultural traditions without rejecting other different traditions.

- Religious beliefs

You won't always be in agreement with parents' beliefs, whether these are part of a religious faith or more personal views on child rearing. Show respect by attempting to understand the beliefs of others. You should offer a courteous explanation if what parents want goes directly against your own values or those of your centre. Of course, disagreements can arise whether or not you share with parents the same culture or religious beliefs.

- Extend your knowledge

You will be more able to learn if you remember that not everyone will have the same social or cultural background as your own. You will find opportunities to learn about different cultures and religious beliefs by talking to other people, reading and by watching films and television.

Boys and girls

In many countries, the UK included, men and women have been treated differently. In childhood, boys and girls have been introduced to different kinds of play activities – as a preparation for adult life.

Inflexible views of what boys and girls should or shouldn't do will restrict their opportunities for learning. Such views can also shake the confidence of children who are not behaving in line with what a boy or girl 'ought' to do.

Good practice combines a respect for children's interests with an active encouragement to try a broad range of play activities. Applying equal opportunities on gender doesn't mean that you stop girls playing with dolls or never let boys play with cars. Workers should remove limits set by rigid views and stretch children's interests and skills.

Children with special needs

All children need affectionate and safe care. Some babies and children have additional individual needs. The term 'special needs' applies to the following kinds of circumstances:

- Some children may have a disability which causes their development to follow a different pattern, or unfold much more slowly, from that of the majority. Examples are children with Down's syndrome or cerebral palsy.

- Some children, although not experiencing physical disabilities, may have a specific learning difficulty. For example, children who are dyslexic need special help with reading and writing.

- Some children may have a continuing health condition that affects their life. The friendships of such children with others may be disturbed because of frequent trips to hospital. There may be some play activities that they cannot join. Examples are children with severe asthma and those with sickle cell anaemia.

Sometimes workers have described the hair or skin care needs of black children as special needs. Using this term is not appropriate because these are ordinary, everyday needs shared by a very large number of children.

2.2 The law and care

United Kingdom legislation sets out what must and cannot be done when caring for young children. All centres have to operate within these laws. A short explanation follows of the legislation that is most likely to be relevant to your job.

The Children Act 1989

This act lays out many specific requirements about the care of children in residential homes and daily centres, for fostering and the resolving of disputes over children in families. Among many other points the Act requires that childminders and groups offering care to children under 8 years old must be registered with the local Social Services Department.

The Children Act is supported by books of guidance issued by the Department of Health. The relevant publication for your work is Volume 2, *Family support, day care and educational provision for young children.* Guidance from the Department explains in detail how centres are expected to organise and deliver services for children and their families.

The volumes of guidance are not law but they describe good practice. Any local authority or centre that acted contrary to the guidance would have to justify their actions.

> **ACTIVITY**
>
> Talk with your supervisor to find out how the Children Act has affected practice at the centre. Your supervisor may have a copy of your local authority's guidelines for standards.

The Race Relations Act 1976

This legislation makes it unlawful to discriminate against anyone on racial grounds. Unlawful discrimination might be very direct, for example, refusing to admit a boy to a nursery because he is black. Or it might be less obvious. For example, a centre might have an admissions policy that discriminates because the catchment area has been drawn so as to exclude a nearby area with many black residents.

The Education Act 1986

Since this act became law it has been illegal to use corporal punishment (for example, caning or hitting) in any *state school* in England, Wales and Scotland. The act does not cover private schools or care settings such as day nurseries.

The Department of Health Guidance issued under the Children Act takes a firm stand that corporal punishment of children should not be used in any care setting, regardless of whether or not such action would be against the law. Your local authority guidelines and centre policy are very likely to support this prohibition.

Health and Safety at Work

Other laws make requirements that should ensure your welfare and safety at work. Examples are the Fire Precautions Act 1971, the Food Safety Act 1990 and the Health and Safety at Work etc. Act 1974 with its statutory regulations. Annexe D to Volume 2 of the Guidance to the Children Act provides more detail if you should need it.

The law and good practice

It is not likely that you will be concerned about detailed legal requirements. If you find you need advice, a good place to start is the Children's Legal Centre, 20 Compton Terrace, London N1 2UN (tel. 071–359–6251).

Laws will not tell you how to do your job in every detail. You must obey the law but you will also develop your own good practice by learning from experienced workers and following the recommendations of experts in child care.

2.3 Continuity of care

ACTIVITY

Start a section in your work file on local centres for children and their families. Your local authority may publish a guide to services. You could try your local library for a copy, or else telephone the under-eights department of Social Services and explain what you want.

    The information you gather will help you if you decide later with your supervisor that you would like to visit a number of different kinds of centre.

A child's first days

Children and their parents will settle more easily if you take some care over the first days and weeks. If parents know what is expected then they can prepare their children.

A child's previous experience

You need to chat with parents and with children who are old enough to have a conversation with you. You will be more able to help each child to settle if you know something of all the children's routines up to the time you meet them, and their likes and dislikes. Find out what sorts of contacts they have had with children and adults outside their own families.

Your wall displays will show the work of the centre

Keeping it personal

Make sure that you know each child's name and how to pronounce it. Does she like to be known by a shortened version? Does he have a favourite cuddly toy or comfort blanket that helps him settle?

A settling-in period

Individual children and their parents will vary in how long they take to become settled and familiar with the new routines, so you need to be flexible in how you organise a settling in period.

Parents and settling in

Most centres encourage a parent, or other carer, to stay with a child for a while to ease the settling-in process. In suggesting how long is a 'while' you need to be sensitive to that person's other responsibilities such as paid work

ACTIVITY

Watch three children during their first week at your centre – not all at the same time. Make notes of any differences between the children in:

1.   Those parts of the routine that children seem to find more difficult.
2.   How quickly each child seems to settle into the group. Make a note of how you have decided that the child seems settled. For example, is it that she has stopped crying or that he will let his mother go.

ACTIVITY

As a worker you are familiar with your care setting. Your memories from childhood may help you to understand how children may be feeling. Think back to your first days as a child at primary school or at a playgroup. Can you remember any part of the routine that surprised you or even upset you?

Make notes of memories that can help you to see your care setting through children's rather than adults' eyes.

or caring for other children. An inflexible timetable won't work since some children will settle more quickly than others.

You can help parents with suggestions on how they could help their child to settle. For example, they can remain sitting when their child starts to explore the setting, rather than following him or her around. You may be able to arrange for a parent to leave the room for short periods, building up to longer amounts of time.

Sometimes it will be the parent who is having difficulty leaving, not the child in letting his parent go. If you haven't gone through this yourself you may not understand the emotions that parents can experience. They may be feeling sad at the prospect of leaving their child or they may be uneasy about handing over responsibility. Some parents may be torn by conflicting emotions – they are pleased that their child is happy in the new setting yet would like to see some signs that they will be missed. You may need advice from your supervisor when a parent seems very reluctant to let go.

Who's responsible when?

Handing over

There must be a clear transfer of responsibility between adults at the beginning and the end of a centre's day. It can be dangerous if workers and parents are uncertain about who is now responsible for watching a young child. Additionally, young children can happily play off one adult against another, if it is unclear who is responsible for getting him into his coat or reprimanding her for an action that she knows is not allowed.

ACTIVITY

Form a pair with another person. One of you takes the role of the worker and one is a parent. Act out a brief exchange based on one of these two situations:

1. The parent has been just putting the child inside the nursery front door and rushing off to work without any contact with a worker.

2. The parent leaves a 5-year-old in the school playground 20 minutes before the start of school.

In each situation, the worker wishes to communicate that the parent's behaviour is unsafe and explain why. The parent gives his or her reasons and doesn't feel in the wrong. The exchange should be discussed with the help of your supervisor.

ACTIVITY

Think about the following situation:

At the end of most days, Keith runs away from his Mum as she tries to get his coat on. He shouts at her and rarely says anything pleasant. She looks embarrassed in her difficulties.

Note down what you could say to help Keith's mother. Discuss your ideas with your supervisor.

Out-of-school services

After-school clubs and centres should have clear procedures on how children pass from being the responsibility of the school to that of the club. If you start work with children aged over 5, make sure that you understand how the handover works. For example, where and when do you meet the children and are there some afternoons when the group has to wait for children who are attending an after-school club?

Who is taking the children?

Part of your responsible handover at the end of each day is knowing who is allowed to take children and who is not.

You should know the general rules of your workplace. For example, many centres for the under-5s will not allow children younger than 12 to take responsibility. The head of your centre should give you specific advice on what to do if some parents are known sometimes to arrive under the influence of drink or drugs.

You should also be informed about any childminding or nanny arrangements made by individual families, and introduced at the first opportunity to anyone else who is allowed to take responsibility for a child.

Some families in conflict will tell you that a particular person, perhaps the parent without custody, is not permitted to take the child at any time. Always check the situation with the head of your centre.

When children move on

Depending on your setting, some children may stay with you for several years which represents a large proportion of their life so far. All the children will leave sooner or later, and you can help to prepare them for the move by talking over with parents how you can best work together.

Parents should visit a new setting and meet their child's worker. You would arrange any introductions to other workers and visits to other rooms within your own centre. Both you and the parent can chat with children about the change that will happen and help them to achieve skills that will ease their way into the next setting. For example, a 4-year-old may need more practice managing alone in the toilet or may express worries about how slowly she does up her shoes.

Not all children feel the same about moving on. Some will be sad but others will be more excited than unhappy.

2.4 Keeping records

All centres should keep written records about the children. If you take a job as a nanny, you should still make notes about the children, their needs and services such as their doctor.

ACTIVITY

Look at the child record forms that are kept at your centre. The form will be laid out with different sections. It may look something like this:

Broomhill Children's Centre – Child Record Form

Child's names: first name(s) James Charles (Charlie)
                  family name   MacIntosh
Date of birth: 15/2/90
Parent(s) name: mother – Debbie MacIntosh (Mrs)
                  father – Andrew MacIntosh
Home address: 5a Dunbar Terrace, Walton
(Mr MacIntosh does not live with the family. He has access and is allowed to collect Charlie.)
Telephone number
Parent(s) work address
           telephone
Child's doctor: name:
                address

And so on...

Setting up a record

All child record forms should include the following:

- The child's name and a note of what he or she is called. For example, Frederick may be called Freddie or Maria Claire Johnston may be known as Claire.
- Date of birth.
- Address of the family.
- Daytime telephone number(s) for contacting parent(s).
- Any significant illnesses that the child has already had, for example, chicken-pox.
- The child's record of inoculation to date.
- The names, addresses and telephone numbers of the child's doctor, local clinic and health visitor.
- A note of who is allowed to collect the child and anyone who is not permitted to do so.
- Matters relevant to care of child such as:
  - daily skin and hair care needs;
  - diet, including any foods that the child is not allowed to eat, is allergic to or dislikes;
  - continuing illness or condition and guidelines for care, for example, what to do if a child with epilepsy has a fit.
- The child's key worker, and any subsequent changes.

ACTIVITY

Ask your supervisor for advice on working with a parent in completing the form used in the centre. Complete a record form with a parent whose child is starting at the centre. Your supervisor or an experienced worker should be present to assist.

Asking parents for information

It's important to take time in completing a basic record with the help of a child's parent. You can ask an experienced worker how long the process usually takes. There will be a lot of questions, and parents may ask why you want to know some information or question who else is likely to read the form. Be ready to explain.

A continuing record

Once children start coming to your centre, other information will go into their records. A proper continuing record of a child should cover:

- Attendance by the child at the centre.
  (Your head of centre should tell you if the absence of any individual child would be a cause for concern and should be reported to her or him.)
- A copy of any written agreement between the centre and the child's parent, with a note of when it should be reviewed.
- Notes on the child's development. The exact format will depend on how the centre makes this assessment.
- Copies of letters relevant to the child.
- Copies of any reports, for example, from a health visitor or speech therapist.

ACTIVITY

Ask your supervisor if your centre uses written agreements with parents. Look at a copy of the form.

Agreements may look something like this:

Child's name: Claire Johnston

Date of agreement: 5 July 1993

Attendance at Brownhill Children's Centre:
Claire will start on 12 July 1993 and attend from 9.30 to 12.00 on Mondays and Tuesdays. Ms Johnston will stay with Claire to settle her for the first two days. She cannot get more days off work. Mr Chandler (father) will take time off work in Claire's second week.

Special concerns:
Claire is 3 years old. She uses very few words and seems not to understand much of what is said to her. Sandra (key worker) will observe Claire in her first 4 weeks.

Review:
Paul (head of centre) and Sandra will meet mother and father at 10.00 on 9 August to discuss:
1. How Claire has settled into the centre
2. Sandra's observations of Claire and parents' opinions
3. A play programme to help Claire
4. Should an appointment be made for a hearing test or speech therapy?

Signed by parent
        head of centre   *key worker*

Access to records

Children's records should not be made available to anyone who does not have a sound reason for looking at them. However, children's parents should have easy access to the records of their own children. An exception is made for what is called 'third party information'. This phrase refers to any reports or letters from professionals outside the centre, for example, a medical report. You cannot make this material accessible to parents without the permission of those other people.

A record of a child is personal and should be put away in the filing cabinet or cupboard when it is not needed. Files should not be left open or lying around in an empty office. If your centre keeps personal information on a computer, this has to be registered under the Data Protection Act. Talk to the head of your centre so that you are clear about how you should follow regulations.

Confidentiality

Responsible workers in any job should not repeat outside their work details that they have learned through the job.

● Who needs to know?
It is important that you don't talk about the personal details of a child or family except with those parents, your supervisor or co-workers who need to know since they have contact with the child or parents.

If you are drawing on your experience of individuals in a course discussion, you can be discreet by using no names or other details which would identify a child or family.

● Polite refusal
If anyone pushes you to discuss details of children or families inappropriately, you are being responsible if you refuse.

Even if people sound official over the telephone, ask politely who they are and their reason for requesting information. You may feel more comfortable saying something like, 'Our centre policy is not to give details over the telephone unless we know the caller'. If you are in any doubt, say that you must consult your senior.

Writing reports

You may not be writing many reports yet. You will be making notes for some of the activities in this book and you may be adding notes to a child's record form. You should bear the following points in mind.

● Are your notes legible?
Other people will need to look at a child's record, so make sure that anything you write is easy to read. Even your personal notes will be no use to you if you can't decipher the scribbles a month later.

● Timely noting
Any notes, however brief, are best made as soon as possible after an event or observation. The longer you leave it, the more your memory is likely to be inaccurate. For example, if you don't make notes this week of how 2-year-old Angela is saying short sentences you will forget the details.

● A separate section on facts
Factual information covers what happened, for example, when Daniel's mother accused the centre staff of hitting her son. Notes of such an event will also include when it happened and who was involved. What people said, written as accurately as possible, may also sometimes form an important part of a record.

ACTIVITY

Find out from the head of your centre under what conditions parents are able to look at their children's records in your setting. For example, do parents have to give notice and does a worker have to be with them while they look?

How are the records organised to deal with the issue of third party information? For instance, such records may be in a separate section that is easy to remove from the file before it is handed to a parent. Make notes in your file.

Information or claims made by other people, but not observed personally by you, should be in a separate section. They may turn out to be reliable, but you don't know this yet.

- Opinions and conclusions

The factual content of a report must not include your guesses about why a child or adult behaved in a certain way. All of your opinions or conclusions should be recorded separately.

Your considered opinion can be valuable. However, it must be made very easy for readers of your reports to distinguish your opinion from the facts on which your opinion is based. Any opinion that you write in notes or reports should be supported by a sentence that includes words such as 'because...' or 'for the following reasons...'.

Reports or notes are not always about troublesome events. You will also be recording children's progress. Your notes about children's development should also distinguish between what children were able to do and the sense you make of this.

Soon your records will describe a child's interests and abilities

Personal notes

Although your personal notes are not accessible to other people, you should still follow the same guidelines when you are writing.

Your personal file or notebook might include any of the following:

- plans and ideas for activities with the children – leave some space to make a brief note of how it went;
- a list of things to do in the near future;
- a note of information you want to find out.

Some centres keep an updated file on local services and useful national organisations. Alternatively, you might like to start a section in your work file for your own reference.

2.5 Working in a team

With co-workers

If you are working in a centre you may have a number of workers on the team, although you may not work closely with more than one or two. The head of your centre is responsible for creating a good atmosphere. All workers need to be sure of what they should be doing and confident about tackling any uncertainties or conflicts that arise. You may have staff group meetings in which to deal with the business and policy of the centre.

Many centres allocate a *key worker* to each child and their parents. The key worker is responsible for keeping the child's records up to date, communicating with parents and organising special programmes for the child. Of course, other workers have contact with the child and parents, but the key worker takes the main responsibility.

It's sensible to consult other workers in order to share ideas and different experiences. In your centre it should be clear how, and on what occasions, you can turn to a senior worker for advice or support.

The head of your centre, if not you personally, will be accountable to any centre management or users' committee. Head teachers have to work with the school governing body.

If you take a job as a nanny you won't have other workers to consult, although you should discuss your work with your employer. Other nannies or friends who work with children in other settings may be able to listen and offer advice. You must respect the family's privacy in any such conversation.

BUILDING A NETWORK AS A NANNY

The Nannies Need Nannies Association can put you in touch with other nannies in your area. Contact them at 28 May Street, South Shields, Tyne and Wear NE33 3AJ (tel: 091–4542617).

The weekly magazine *Nursery World* organises an annual conference for nannies each October. Contact it at 51 Calthorpe Street, London WC1X 0HH (tel: 071–837–7224).

Working with other professionals

Several types of services are responsible for the care and welfare of children and their families. As a result you are likely to have contact with professionals from the education system, health services, local social services and perhaps with special units for children with disabilities.

The Children Act 1989 makes a point of requiring cooperation between different services and professions for the good of children. You can recognise that other people have special expertise and still respect your own skills.

Families involved with several services

Some families have many professionals involved in their lives. Perhaps a son or daughter has a disability that involves visits to the hospital, the help of a physiotherapist or the involvement of Social Services.

If you feel that a parent is becoming overwhelmed with information or is receiving contradictory advice, raise the matter with your supervisor. She or he may be able to help in easing the burden on the family.

3 Contact and communication

Communication is central to good work with children and their parents. We all communicate in one way or another, but not always as well as we might. This chapter focuses on:

- basic elements of good communication;
- special considerations in communicating with children;
- how to build a working relationship with parents.

3.1 Communication

Courteous and effective communication is an exchange of information and opinions. If you talk considerably more than you listen, you won't give children or adults a chance to express what they feel. On the other hand, if you say very little at all people will wonder if you are attending to them.

How to listen

Giving your full attention

Neither children nor adults believe that you are listening if you seem absorbed in other activities while they are talking. They will also feel that you don't value what they have to say if you cut across their words – perhaps to catch the attention of another person.

If you need to write down what a parent is telling you then you should say, 'I'd like to make a note of that, please'. You should explain to parents about written records – their purpose and how you maintain confidentiality – in your first meeting.

Dealing with interruptions

Work with children is full of interruptions, and sometimes it will be unsafe if you fail to stop a child in some action. You will show respect by apologising and helping the conversation to start again. You might say something like, 'I'm sorry. I could see that Andy was about to pull the books on top of his head. You were just telling me that you think Siobhan may be allergic to eggs'.

Encouraging gestures

You will encourage children or adults to continue by brief smiles and nods. You show that you have been listening when your next comment builds on

ACTIVITY

Take turns with a partner to be speaker or listener in two minute conversations. A third person is observer and time keeper. The topic of the conversation can be either 'My best holiday ever' or 'How I started working with children'.

When you are the listener concentrate on what your partner is saying and make only brief comments to encourage your partner to continue. At the end of the two minutes you should summarise as accurately as possible what your partner has told you and the feelings that they communicated.

Discuss the exercise with your partner and the observer considering:

● How accurate was the summary made by the listener?
● Did the summary include feelings and factual events?
● Did the listener comment enough or leave too long a time before saying anything? Two minutes will seem very long if a listener has been silent.

Your feelings will show even if you say nothing

what they have told you, or you ask a question about what they have said. Children and adults will wonder if you really were listening if you don't say anything about what they have just told you.

Reflecting back and summarising

You should check your understanding by reflecting back briefly what you have been told. For example, Mrs James may be telling you she is worried about how little her daughter seems to eat. You should reflect back using your own words – don't repeat Mrs James' exact words. You might say, 'You feel worried because Anthea eats hardly anything all weekend'.

The technique of reflecting back shows that you have been attending and it will help you to remember the details of the conversation as well as making sure that you have understood. After you have reflected back what you have heard, the other person may tell you more or you may ask a short question or offer a practical suggestion – depending on how far the conversation has developed.

Another useful technique is to summarise briefly at the end of a conversation. For example, when the parent has finished talking about Siobhan's possible allergy, the worker might say, 'Would you like us to make sure Siobhan doesn't eat any eggs for the time being?'

Body language

Everyone sends unspoken messages by facial expression, body posture and gestures. Some people have more expansive gestures than others, and there are some cultural differences that we discuss later in this section. It is important that you are aware of body language. Your awareness will help you to communicate more effectively and also to be more sensitive to what other people are showing but not saying directly.

You are far more likely to notice other people's habits in gestures or expressions than to be aware of what you typically do. For example:

● Perhaps you notice that a co-worker often folds her arms tightly in front of her when she is talking with a parent. You feel this may be giving parents the impression that she is ready to criticise, especially since she rarely smiles. You know her well and have found her friendly – but she doesn't look it.
● Unknown to you, you may have a habit during a conversation of looking over someone's shoulder rather than at his or her face. Co-workers or close friends will be able to give you some clues about your body language if you ask them.

Careful interpretations

Both adults and children are aware of body language but cannot always explain their impressions. For example:

● A child might say she doesn't like someone, and when pressed, she says 'He doesn't have smiley eyes'.
● You might wonder how it is that a particular doctor puts children and parents so at ease in the developmental checks. Then you realise that he listens with his full attention; he never writes notes as someone is speaking.

You will need to talk to your supervisor if you have an uneasy feeling about a child or parent. You cannot decide whether you are right to be concerned and whether any action is needed unless you can identify exactly what you have noticed.

Don't come to premature conclusions about what someone is like as a person just from what they do. For example, a parent who is not at all confident may seem brusque or reluctant to speak to you. The behaviour appears to be rude yet that is not the intention.

Culture and body language

Some differences in body language are shared by many individuals within the same culture. People have learned certain gestures and have been told as children that to behave in a particular way is polite. Since the UK is a multicultural society, you need to understand that such differences exist. An example follows:

● Looking directly at other people
Children in the UK and the USA are usually encouraged to look at other people. Indeed, adults in these countries sometimes conclude that a child who won't look you in the eye has something to hide.

Children from some other countries, for example, Japan and some parts of Africa and the West Indies, are taught the opposite – that it is more polite to look downwards, unless you know someone very well.

What can you do?

The most important thing is to avoid jumping to conclusions. If children or adults are from a different culture to yourself, it's possible that you are misunderstanding what is to them normal and polite behaviour. You should raise any concerns with your supervisor. A worker who is from the same culture as the child or other adult may be able to advise you.

It's not possible to act in a way that is guaranteed never to break a cultural rule for somebody, somewhere. There are some sensible rules you can follow – regardless of whether other people's body language is influenced by their culture or by their individual preferences:

1. Be sensitive to the body language signals of other people. If someone wants more or less distance between the two of you as you speak, try to compromise by moving forward or back a little. You do not, of course, have to tolerate feeling really uncomfortable.

2. It is probably wiser to avoid touching workers or parents until you know them well. Touch children gently and be alert to how close they wish to be to you. Respect their wishes.

3. Be sparing in using hand gestures to convey simple messages like 'OK'. Some innocent gestures in one culture carry a rude meaning in another. Be cautious about using gestures to beckon an adult from a distance. It is better to wave in greeting and then go to speak with him or her. Some cultures have firm rules about gestures that should only be used to children and never between adults.

Special approaches

Different languages or accents

It is much harder to communicate clearly if two people don't share a language. Even the same language spoken with a different accent and word order can lead to confusion. You can help by taking your time and by these guidelines:

● Use simpler words and shorter sentences. Be ready to repeat what you have said and take any opportunity to show what you mean as you speak.

ACTIVITY

Work in pairs to explore how it's possible to send a different message using the same words but varying your body language and your tone of voice.

Take turns to be the speaker or the listener.

1. A worker is speaking to a parent.
   The worker says, 'You're late again this morning'.
   Firstly, make the message like an accusation. Then say the same words with a more sympathetic message – thinking perhaps of the awful bus service.

2. A worker is speaking to a 3 year old.
   The worker says, 'You've really done your best with that picture'.
   Firstly make the praise sound sincere, then make it sound half-hearted.

Discuss the exercise. As a listener what did you observe? How did your partner's gestures or facial expression change? What have you learned?

ACTIVITY

Discuss with your supervisor how many different languages are spoken locally. How many of these are represented by families who attend the centre? Are there any local translation or interpretation services? Make a note in your file.

- If you go more slowly, the other person may match your pace. You will then have more chance of understanding what is said to you in return.
- Take pauses, so that the other person can digest what you have said. Give an opportunity for him or her to ask questions to help understanding.
- Do take advantage of anyone who can help you out, for instance, an older child in the family or a bilingual worker.

Disabilities affecting communication

Some children and adults will have disabilities that affect their communication skills. You should definitely get specialist advice and support if you are working with children with disabilities.

If parents have a loss of hearing or vision, you need to adjust the way that you communicate:

- You should look directly at any parents who have partial or total loss of hearing. They need to see your face for the additional clues of expression and to lip read if they are able.
- Parents with visual disabilities may appreciate an initial, friendly touch on the arm and a word of introduction, particularly if they are unlikely to recognise your voice.
- If parents or other visitors are in a wheelchair, it is courteous to sit so that you maintain level eye contact and don't literally talk down to them.

You can ask people what they would find helpful in your behaviour. If you have a disability that affects your communication then make practical suggestions to parents when you first meet them.

3.2 Communication with children

You will communicate well with children if you apply your skills in talking and listening with special consideration for children's physical size and their current abilities in communication.

Get close

Close enough to touch

Babies and toddlers will not realise that you are communicating with them unless you are facing them and are close enough to touch them. Babies enjoy the affectionate communication that is shown through cuddling and chatting with them long before they can understand your words.

Young children move physically close to adults who show warmth through their communication. You will have experienced already how many children like to hold your hand or sit on your lap. Whatever the cultural traditions of behaviour learned by older children, young children tend to get close unless other adults have abused their trust in the past.

Contact through care routines

You will be in close contact with babies and toddlers as you change and feed them. Chapter 6 covers the routine for physical care and the opportunities that it offers for gentle touch, smiles and chat. Friendly communication should also be part of your care routines for slightly older children. Chapter 7 will help you think about running a social mealtime or the importance of communication as you help a child to become toilet trained.

Getting children's attention

Young babies can be distressed if you appear suddenly, so speak gently to them as you move into their line of vision. If you are playing with a small group of children, you have to get the attention of individuals – by using names or a touch on the arm – before you start to speak. Otherwise you can be halfway through a sentence before a child realises that you are addressing her this time.

Get on the same eye level

Children are shorter than adults. They will have to look up at you if you don't sit down or bend at the knees. Ideally, you want to be face to face in order to communicate well with anyone.

Talking with children

The same basic guidelines work in communication with children as much as with adults. The following additional tips are important when you are working with children under 8 years old:

- Keep your language simple – use short sentences and pause for children to reply or show that they have become confused. You should still pause and look expectant when you are chatting with babies and toddlers who don't speak yet – they will 'tell' you something in reply.

ACTIVITY

Watch an experienced worker who is skilled in talking with children. What does this person do? For example, does she bend down to the children's height or does he show enthusiasm when children speak?

Discuss with this worker what he or she thinks is most important in encouraging children in communication. Make notes on what you have learned.

Children feel you're interested when you sit at their level

- Use simple words and be ready to repeat what you've said in an even simpler way. Most 5-year-olds and even some 4-year-olds will start to ask the meaning of words that they don't know.
- Be ready to show what you want as well as say it.
- Tell children if you have not understood what they have said. Encourage them to expand on their first remark or to show you what they mean if that is possible.

Taking their interests seriously

Children get bored if adults are only interested in what they, themselves, want to communicate. Make sure that you give children the time and opportunity to tell you about what interests them:

- You should usually react with equal enthusiasm to topics that children introduce in general conversation. They may be keen to tell you how they saw a squirrel in the park or what they did over the weekend. If a child is sharing horrible details of pulling the legs off spiders, you can express your feeling that you don't think that's a kind thing to do. You should talk with your supervisor if a child's topics of conversation worry you.
- Your facial expression will show that you are paying attention and you can smile your encouragement as well.
- You also show you are really interested by making comments and by asking questions. Sometimes it will feel right to repeat what a child has said with an enthusiastic sound in your voice.
- You show genuine interest by referring later to what a child told you, for example, you might say the following day, 'I saw a squirrel this morning. I wonder if it was the same one you saw yesterday'.

Time and effort

You show respect for children by making an effort. For instance, you may not be as interested as they are in a particular television programme; you may even be concerned that children are taking some programmes far too seriously. However, you won't help to widen their interests if you're dismissive about their current passion. You'll get further by watching a couple of episodes so you can comment as well.

Handling interruptions

You also show your interest by courteous treatment of children in your communication. Don't let other adults break into your conversation with a child or divert your attention in a way that would be rude between adults. If you have to interrupt a child, apologise and then help her to get back to what she was saying.

Children will learn to communicate with confidence if you don't look as if you are in a rush. There will be times when you have to deal with something else immediately, for example, mopping up a large spill on the floor before someone steps in it. As soon as you are able, do try to give the attention that a child wants.

At other times you may need to explain to a child that you would like to chat so long as he realises that you have to clear the table. Under these circumstances even 3-year-olds are often pleased to watch you and chat. Older children may be able to help and talk at the same time.

Sharing yourself out

You should be fair in sharing out your time between children. Try to avoid creating the situation where the child who shouts loudest gets most of your attention. Make the first move to the child who doesn't ask outright for your attention. You won't warm to all children equally but it is unfair if you have favourites within a group. You should talk with your supervisor if you find it very hard to relate to a child.

ACTIVITY

If you are working with children over 3 years old, then choose one child and over a week keep a note of the topics of any conversations that he or she *starts* with you.

Your record might look like this:

Conversations with Jason (five years old) 2–6 June

Monday 2nd – baby brother was sick this morning all over Mum; what happened in his favourite Saturday morning television programme.

Tuesday 3rd – saw a fire engine on the way to the centre. And so on...

At the end of the week look over your notes. What topics did this child want to share with you? Would it be helpful to watch Jason's favourite programme to understand what he's talking about?

3.3 Developing a relationship with parents

Remind yourself that section 3.1 applies to communication with parents as well as with other workers. Parents are not some odd breed of human being that requires a completely different technique. It is important to recall, however, that you come together with parents through your work with their children. You have not chosen each other as friends; you are seeking to establish a friendly working relationship.

Value each other's expertise

You are in a job that announces that you have expertise with children. Some parents may be wary of you if they don't feel confident in themselves. Because of their previous experience, they may expect you to be critical, or to tell them what to do. You can build a positive relationship by making sure that you listen to parents' views and offer any suggestions as possibilities and not as instructions.

You may be fairly clear about what it's like to work with young children. Perhaps you would like parents to understand your job better and perhaps appreciate how hard you work. On the other hand, do you understand what it's like to be a parent?

There are parallels between working with and parenting children under 8 but the two tasks are not the same. If you have children of your own, then you know what parenting means to you but you may not be aware of what it is like to raise children under different family circumstances or in a different cultural tradition.

Children need families

Different kinds of families

Children need affectionate and consistent care from parents who take a long-term responsibility through childhood and adolescence. Children need parents to care deeply about what happens to them yet they can flourish in a variety of family situations. For instance:

- Some families have two parents. These may be the biological parents of the children, but might also be step-parents, foster or adoptive parents.

- Some families are headed by a lone parent – more usually mothers than fathers. Some children may no longer see the other parent but in other cases there will be contact.

- Most parents will be heterosexual but some fathers will be gay and some mothers lesbian.

- Parents may have a paid job as well as all the work of parenting. Women may be the breadwinners as well as or instead of the men.

- Some families include other generations and relatives, living together in an extended family.

Families and different cultural traditions

In your contact with parents you may come across ways of life and beliefs that are new to you. You should take time to understand when parents' culture or religious beliefs will have practical implications for the care of their child. A note of the parents' wishes should go in the child's record.

ACTIVITY

The best way to increase your understanding of parenting will be through talking with adults who are parents. Perhaps some workers in the centre have children of their own. Learn from what they share with you willingly but be careful not to ask a lot of intrusive questions. Ask your supervisor for advice if there are particular aspects to parenting that you wish to understand.

You need to be careful in how you generalise from this information, especially if you use it to predict what another family may want for their child. For example, you may describe three families as 'Asian' yet one family may have come originally from India, the second from Pakistan and the third from Uganda. They are unlikely to follow the same religion or share a language other than English.

First contact with parents

Centres vary in how they handle the first contact with parents. Find out what happens in your centre – for example:

- Are parents invited to visit the centre before accepting a place?
- Do workers visit families at home before a child attends?
- Is there any written material, like a brochure, that is given to parents whose children attend?

You are getting to know parents as well as children

> ### ACTIVITY
>
> Ask your supervisor for permission to attend a first meeting between parents and the centre. Make a short list of what you wish to observe:
>
> 1. What topics are raised with the parents?
> 2. What questions do they ask?
> 3. How does the worker in charge of the meeting try to put parents at their ease?
>
> In the meeting you should be introduced to parents and an explanation given of why you will be making notes. After the meeting is over ask the worker for her or his opinion of the meeting. Was it unusual in any way?

If you work in a local authority day nursery or family centre, some parents may be referred through the local social services. Talk with your supervisor about sensitive, early contact with parents who may feel obligated to bring their child and perhaps also attend themselves. How do experienced workers deal with parents' possible feelings of resentment or their anxiety that their parenting skills are doubted?

Early weeks

> ### ACTIVITY
>
> Talk with a parent whom you know fairly well. Ask him or her about the first days of contact with your centre. Does this parent have practical suggestions, based on experience, for making other parents feel welcome and at ease? Take notes and consider whether some changes might improve the early weeks for parents.

Names

People's names are important and the care you take will help a relationship start well:

He can't say how his day has gone – so you must tell his parents

- At your first opportunity, introduce yourself by name to parents as well as to their children. If your name could be unfamiliar, then be ready to repeat it.

- Make sure that you have got a parent's name right. Check that you're saying and writing it correctly. The same care is needed, of course, for checking children's names.

- Some centres have a policy of addressing everyone by first name. Not everyone is comfortable with this informality, so be sensitive if a parent or grand-parent prefers to be addressed by title and surname.

- Cultures differ in the ordering of personal and family name. So, if you have only seen a child's name written down, make sure that you have the different names sorted out.

Exchange of information

Within the first weeks, parents need to have heard and understood basic information about your centre such as times, the clothes that children need and the behaviour that is expected of adults – for instance, most centres for children don't allow smoking in the play areas. Remember that parents will be taking in a lot of information in a short space of time. People do not generally remember everything under these circumstances. You can help by:

- being ready to repeat, politely, relevant information about the centre;

- having a conversation or meeting with parents after their child has attended for a couple of weeks to sort out anything that they would like to ask, or that you would like to make clear.

Everyday contact

Talking together

You can't share the care of babies and children unless you have opportunities to communicate with parents. You are busy and so are parents since they have their own schedule to follow. Some parents may be more able or inclined to stay to chat than others. It is important that you build up friendly contact. Then asking a question or expressing a concern is less likely to make parents feel threatened.

You can establish a good working relationship with the following approaches:

- Express a welcome and a sense of friendliness by a smile and a wave to parents across a room. As far as possible recognise that they have arrived and when they are leaving.

- Make the opportunity to chat, even briefly, with parents about the enjoyable events of the day for their child. You would feel very disheartened if parents only made the effort to talk with you if there was a problem. You might be pleased to say that Daniel has got over his fear of the hamster or that Sian made a magnificent dragon from the junk materials.

- You don't always have to talk about the children. You might ask a parent if she's feeling better after the flu or express fellow-feeling about the teeming rain outside.

- If you want to have a longer conversation with a parent, then it's sensible to check first on a convenient time. You might say, 'I'd like to talk with you about Tony and how he's settling in. Have you got a short while now?' If the answer is 'no', then find a time convenient to both of you.

- A parent might want to talk over something specific with you. Don't feel that you must respond at length whenever a parent asks. It's better to be honest, if you really don't have time at that moment. If you carry on with a conversation, knowing you should be elsewhere, your body language will betray you. Instead say something like, 'I'm sorry I have to take a group of children now, but I could talk with you this afternoon when you pick Beverley up'.
- Do make the effort to involve children, even toddlers, in simple conversations with their parents, for example, about the painting they have done. You should discuss any problems you are experiencing with a child in a private conversation with a parent.

Using words

You and your co-workers will use words and phrases about children's care or development that seem ordinary to you; however, they may not be part of everyday conversation for other adults, including parents. For example, you may talk about children's hand–eye coordination but parents are more likely to focus on specific skills such as drawing or writing.

Modifying your use of words in conversation with parents isn't talking down to them. You're being courteous to recognise that everyone doesn't use language in the same way.

Questions and advice

A mother or father may ask your advice on some aspect of baby or child care. Perhaps the child doesn't seem to be eating much at mealtimes at home. Answer the parent simply, using everyday language. You can share any suggestions about which you are confident, perhaps explaining to the parent how such a situation is handled in the centre.

Sometimes a parent may ask your advice but what he or she is asking is outside your experience. If you don't know the answer or are unsure, it is better to say so. Find out and then pass on any advice later.

Confidentiality

Parents should be able to trust that what they say to you will never be passed on as gossip – either within your centre or outside the job. It is appropriate that you should repeat details of a conversation to another worker who is also involved with the child or family. This other worker is, like you, sharing the care of the child with the parent. He or she needs to know.

Sometimes you may be placed in a difficult position by parents who confide worrying information about the child or their family circumstances yet ask you to promise not to tell anyone else. You should explain that you cannot keep secrets in your job and that you are obligated to share with the head of your centre anything that seriously affects the children. You could say to the parent, 'I will have to tell my head about this or would you like to tell her/him yourself?'

Disagreements with parents

Communication problems are possible. Any two people sharing the care of the same children can disagree – it certainly happens within families. Differences of opinion don't have to become serious problems so long as you are prepared to work with parents for good communication.

If the disagreement has resulted from a misunderstanding, try to clear this up as fast as possible. Talk with your supervisor afterwards to learn how you might reduce or avoid future misunderstandings.

ACTIVITY

Ask your supervisor how you should make appointments to speak at greater length with parents. Is there a room in the centre suitable for private conversations with parents? Make a note in your file of the arrangements.

ACTIVITY

1. Talk with your supervisor about avoiding words that may sound like jargon to parents. Note down the suggestions in your work file.
2. Take a friend who doesn't work with children to look at the displays in your centre or show your friend a non-confidential report that you have written. Ask him or her to point out words or phrases that are unfamiliar – either as words or in the way that you are using the words.

ACTIVITY

It may not be appropriate for you to continue some conversations with a parent unless someone more senior is also involved. Talk with your supervisor to find out under what circumstances she or he would expect you to seek support. This will certainly be the case if a parent says or implies that a child is at risk in some way.

Some parents may disagree with the way in which you are providing care for their children. Listen carefully and ask questions to make sure that you have grasped the point they are making. Use the technique of summarising briefly at the end of the conversation to check your understanding.

If you can follow parents' wishes in the care of their child then do so. For example, you may not have realised that their daughter has been distressed by having to strip down to her underwear for dance – the skin on her legs is seriously affected by eczema and the other children stare. You don't want to let her sit out of dance altogether, but you can reach a compromise on what she wears.

On other occasions, a request may be contrary to centre policy. For example, parents may complain that you allow their son to play with dolls which they believe is inappropriate. You will need to explain the policy once more, with the reasons. Enlist the support of your supervisor if necessary. Certainly, don't leave a parent with the impression that you will follow what they ask when you definitely will not.

ACTIVITY

In pairs take turns in the role of worker and of parent to practise giving an explanation of centre policy. A third person should observe.

1. The parent's role
   You want the worker to slap your daughter if she misbehaves. You insist that you are giving permission, so what is the problem? You believe that children run wild without this kind of discipline.

2. The worker's role
   You are explaining in simple terms why no worker is allowed to use physical forms of punishment on the children. Try to give an example of how you handle the kind of difficult behaviour that concerns this parent.

Discuss how the conversations developed. Can you now think of a better way for the worker to explain?

3.4 Running a group for parents

You need to think in a slightly different way about communication if you are asked to run a group for parents. As well as all the points made so far, you will need to be aware of what makes any group work well and what can get in the way.

What is the purpose of the group?

Suppose that several parents approach you or your supervisor about having a group in your centre. You will need to discuss with these parents what they want from the group before you could agree to make any arrangements. For example:

- Are parents hoping that the group will be largely social – a source of company and conversation?
- Do they want meetings to which you invite local professionals for an information session?

If the idea for a parents' group comes from your supervisor or other workers, then you all need to be very clear about your aims, before you start asking parents if they wish to join in. For example:

- Are you planning an educational purpose to the group, for instance, sharing child care skills with parents?
- Is your supervisor hoping that parents will meet on a regular basis and help make materials for the centre or raise funds?

It is crucial that you are honest about the purpose of any group that is started by the centre. Parents may choose not to join the kind of group that you propose, and you cannot conclude from this that they are uninterested in any kind of involvement in your centre. They are just saying, 'No thank you' to this group.

How will the group run?

You will need to sort out practical details:

- Where will the group meet and when?
- How long will meetings last?
- Will there be refreshments?
- Is smoking allowed in the room where the group will meet, and what about non-smokers?
- After how many meetings will the group review the progress of the group and whether to continue?

These questions may seem obvious but promising groups have faltered over minor irritations or people getting confused about what is going on and when.

One worker should remain responsible for the group. Parents will then get to know that person and she or he will be able to guide the group in the knowledge of what has happened in previous meetings. A necessary change in worker should be handled courteously with the group members.

Running the group

If you are responsible for a group, you need to be clear about your role. You should discuss this with your supervisor before the first meeting and be ready to consult with her or him regularly between meetings:

- You are responsible for the group but your role does not mean you should dominate meetings by talking a lot of the time. You will need to ensure that meetings go as smoothly as possible and keep an eye on the time. You might be the one to make sure that the more talkative members don't squeeze out the quieter ones.

- Even if most decisions are taken by the parents in the group, there may be some non-negotiable ground rules. A group being run in your centre shouldn't contravene centre policy in its membership or activities.

- The head of your centre might stress that a social group must remain open to new people; it mustn't turn into an exclusive club for the first group of parents. On the other hand, a support group for parents who have experienced a particular kind of difficulty might be run for an agreed number of meetings with the same group members.

- If the group is intended to be an opportunity for parents to talk about their children or family life, you will need clear rules on confidentiality that are agreed by all group members.

ACTIVITY

Talk with an experienced worker who has run a group for parents. What practical advice would this person offer? Ask questions and take notes on what went well with the group and what problems emerged. How were difficulties overcome?

4 Health and well-being

This chapter deals with your responsibilities:

* to keep children safe;
* to be alert to threats to children's health and well-being;
* to take care of your own well-being as a worker.

4.1 Keeping children safe

Even if you are very careful and well organised in your setting, some children will still have minor accidents. Both 2- and 3-year-olds have no sense of danger, and even children older than 5 may not foresee a risk in what they want to do.

It's important that you teach young children about common dangers in their environment. They will slowly learn how to take good care of themselves, but don't expect even 7-year-olds always to remember the rules you have taught them.

Standards for safety

The head of your centre will be responsible for ensuring that the centre building and all the equipment meet the standards described in Volume 2 of the Department of Health Guidance to the Children Act 1989 – *Family support, day care and educational provision for young children*. In this section we are describing some of the points to which you should pay careful attention as a worker.

Kitchens

These are an essential area for any care setting but are a source of risk to children. Even adults manage to have such accidents as cutting or burning themselves while working in the kitchen. A kitchen in a care setting for children should be equipped with all possible safety features such as cooker guards and child locks on cupboards.

In group care, children are often totally kept out of the kitchen. If you do allow children into the kitchen you must supervise them very carefully and make a safe area for them to sit, for example, around a kitchen table.

Bathrooms

Younger children should not be unsupervised in the toilet or washroom, any more than in the kitchen. They will need help in going to the toilet and a reminder to wash their hands. Water should never emerge from a tap at a

Centres have to follow high standards of hygiene

temperature that makes it hot. If it does then you should find out from a senior worker how to adjust the thermostat on the water system.

Each child should have his or her own comb or brush, flannel and towel in order to avoid cross infection. These personal items should be marked with pictures and names.

Play materials and equipment

Play materials should only be bought from reputable companies and should conform to British safety standards, whenever these apply. You should check toys and equipment regularly. If something needs mending, for example, torn dressing up clothes or a screw that needs tightening, then make the repair promptly. Check with a senior worker if any equipment looks to you as if it needs specialist attention or is in your opinion beyond repair.

Babies and toddlers suck and chew many of their play materials so it is especially important that their toys are regularly washed in hot soapy water, rinsed and left to drip dry. Rattles and similar baby toys should not pass from baby to baby without being cleaned.

When you lay out or tidy up toys and play materials for older children, you should check whether they need cleaning. Your storage system for all toys should keep out dust as far as possible.

Outside space

Babies and children enjoy the variety offered by outdoor play as well as indoor. All garden and outdoor space must be secure so that children cannot wander off, and should be free from hazards like unfenced ponds or sharp sticks. Young children may put unclean objects and earth into their mouths, so you must watch them all the time.

You will be taking children on trips to parks and other places which you cannot expect to be as safe as the centre. Keep children safe by knowing as much as you can of the place you are visiting and by keeping alert during the visit.

Preventive hygiene

Strict standards of hygiene are needed for kitchen and bathroom areas. Infections, especially those causing stomach upsets, can pass swiftly through a group of children. The head of your centre is responsible for ensuring that kitchen staff and cleaners maintain the standards.

You should wash your hands thoroughly with soap, or an alternative if you are allergic to soap, under these conditions:

- after changing a child;
- before cleaning cuts or grazes;
- after you have been to the toilet;
- before you handle food or prepare a baby's bottle.

You should cover any cuts or grazes on your hands with a plaster. Any further precautions to prevent cross infection from blood or waste products should always be applied when caring for children. In this way you will not make children with known health problems feel uncomfortably different from the rest of the group.

It is important to remember that you don't have to appear to be uncaring as you follow careful procedures. You should talk to and smile at a baby whom you are changing, and you should comfort a child who is bleeding. Explain simply to any child, or adult, who asks about precautions such as plastic gloves that you come into contact with so many children that it's too easy to pass on germs without realising it.

ACTIVITY

Ask your supervisor about centre policy for the ratio of children to workers on trips. Make notes like this:

- Going to the local shops
  — children over 3 years with one adult;
  — children under 3 years with one adult.
- Trip to the swimming pool
  — children with one adult.

And so on.

ACTIVITY

Ask your supervisor to explain centre policy on hygiene especially about changing children and dealing with cuts and grazes:

1. Are you required to use disposable plastic gloves?
2. What should you do with used gloves, disposable nappies and bandages?

Make notes in your work file.

Play is untidy

Children will have a miserable time if they are expected to keep play materials tidy all the time. Nor is it realistic to expect children always to sit up neatly to table activities. Games with bricks and cars are often more fun when played on the floor.

Children need to spread themselves out and many creative activities, like play dough or painting, cannot be enjoyed without some mess. Materials such as sand and water will get tipped and spilled, and so clearing up is part of the end of most activities.

Be ready to tidy and clear up, with the children's involvement, at intervals through the day. Sometimes your aim will be to make some space, rather than insist that everything gets put back in the right box. You don't have to let the routine spoil the children's day. For example, you can put a child's construction to one side to be admired later rather than demolish everything because it's snack time.

Constant vigilance

Experienced workers with children under 8 years old rightly say that 'you need eyes in the back of your head'. Unfortunately, you won't be equipped with these, so you have to use all the senses that you do have. When you look and listen carefully it will sometimes be the suspicious absence of noise that alerts you.

Babies and toddlers should never be completely out of everyone's sight, unless they are asleep, in which case they should not be out of hearing and you should check on their well-being during their nap.

Who's in charge?

It must always be absolutely clear who is responsible for a group of children. If you are called away or are taking a break, you must explicitly pass responsibility for your group to another centre worker – don't just assume that someone will keep an eye on the children.

Appropriate equipment will help you to keep children safe

On any trips away from the centre, make sure that all workers and any parents who are helping know exactly which children are their responsibility on this trip. If you are the worker in overall charge you should be very clear in your instructions about where and when small groups will meet up for the journey home. Keep a list of children and adults who have come on the trip and check for everyone before moving on.

Dealing with accidents

Children will get hurt on occasion, however safe the setting and however careful the adults. As well as remembering the standards for hygiene, there are several other things to do if a child is hurt:

- Immediate first aid

Use the appropriate contents of the centre first aid box to clean cuts and grazes and to cover them if necessary. Be ready to call another worker for assistance if you should need help.

Find out which centre workers have had first aid training and complete a course yourself as soon as possible. The Red Cross and the St John's Ambulance Brigade often run local courses.

- Comfort the child

You can comfort a child who is hurt at the same time that you offer whatever care is needed. Sometimes children are more shaken up than hurt. Sometimes they may be expecting you to be angry, since they have been careless or have knowingly broken a rule. You can reassure them of your concern for them and still emphasise kindly that this was why you warned 'Don't walk behind the swing'.

Even if you believe that a child is making rather a fuss, accept her feelings as she expresses them. Look for an opportunity to praise her if she takes a braver outlook. Don't expect a boy to be more able to hold back tears than a girl of the same age. Never tell a child, 'It doesn't hurt!'; you have no way of knowing.

- Later – deal with any practical issues

You may decide that the whole group needs a reminder about safe behaviour in the garden. Choose your timing and your words, so that you don't embarrass the child who was most recently hurt.

If the problem has arisen from faulty or broken equipment, remove it immediately or mark it clearly 'not to be used'. Inform your supervisor.

- Making notes

All centres should have accident books. It would be wise to have some way of making notes if you work as a nanny.

- Tell parents

You should inform parents when they collect their child if he or she has had an accident, even a minor graze. Explain what happened and how you treated the cut or bruise. Tell them if it is not centre policy to clean wounds with antiseptic since parents may wish to do this when they get home.

Most parents will be understanding about everyday bumps and scrapes, if they are told promptly. The most cooperative parents can be cross when they find unexplained bruises later. Parents will also want to know that you are going to deal effectively with, for instance, a child who bites others.

Crises and emergencies

Fire

You should know exactly how to get yourself and the children out of the building in the event of fire. A centre should have regular drills – you may be told the day but not the time of the drill. You should know the location of the centre fire alarms and extinguishers.

If you are working as a nanny, you should have precautionary equipment such as a fire extinguisher and fire blanket easily available in the kitchen. You are responsible for taking precautions against fire, for example, during cooking.

ACTIVITY

Your centre may have rules about what, if anything, is put on children's cuts and bruises. Check out this information with experienced workers and make a note of the information.

Children get over minor accidents quite quickly

ACTIVITY

Look at the accident book in your centre.

Ask your supervisor under what circumstances notes should be made and who should make them.

Write up an accident with help from your supervisor or an experienced worker.

ACTIVITY

Talk over with your supervisor what would *not* be worth reporting to parents.

Talk over also what kind of accident should lead you immediately to contact parents during the day. Do you know how to find emergency telephone numbers for a parent in a child's file?

Dealing with aggression or violence

You may never have to deal with anything more unpleasant than a parent who gets irritated or angry with you. Under these circumstances you should remain as calm as possible – don't shout in retaliation and certainly don't trade insults. Part of your job is to be patient and attempt to understand what is being said, even if it isn't said pleasantly.

Show that you are listening to what is said and give your replies briefly, at normal volume. If it is possible for you to do something to resolve the situation that led to this person's anger, then explain simply what you will be doing. If there is no practical course of action for you to take or the argument is really over centre policy, then suggest firmly that this person should speak with the head of centre.

Some centres work with parents who are known to turn to violence under stress or the influence of alcohol. The aggressive behaviour of such people can get swiftly out of control. You must know how to call for additional help and be ready to get yourself and the children out of the room if such an action will protect you all. The safety of the children and your welfare are more important that any potential damage to property.

Talk with your supervisor so that you understand the procedure in your centre. You should also have the opportunity to attend training on ways to deal with angry or violent people. There are sensible approaches to take, but unfortunately no single correct way to handle any explosive situation.

4.2 Health and illness

Children will get ill sometimes, just as they will have minor accidents. You should know what to do when children fall ill while they are your responsibility. You should also be aware of the specific health problems of any children, by talking with their parents and reading the notes in their files.

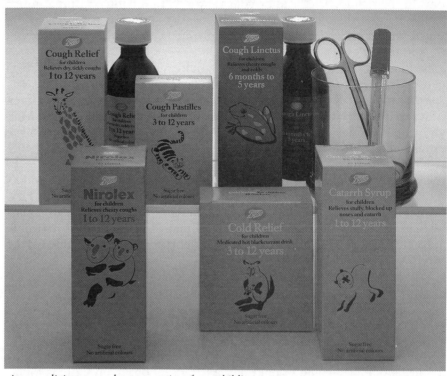

Any medicines must be appropriate for a child's age

When children fall ill

How ill?

You need to be competent in taking children's temperature and in assessing whether babies and children are unwell. 3- or 4-year-olds will be able to tell you how they feel, but they may not be accurate in their use of names for parts of the body. Ask them to show you where it hurts or aches. Be ready to consult other workers or your supervisor.

Groups of young children pass round colds, coughs and other illnesses to each other and to workers. Catching one cold after another is an exhausting experience in itself. Children who have many colds often get ear infections which can lead to glue ear. This condition can affect their hearing and therefore their capacity to learn. Consult your supervisor and a child's parents if children appear to have difficulty hearing you although the room is quiet.

Who needs to know if a child is ill?

- Parents

Obviously, you need to contact parents if their child is ill and your supervisor agrees with you that the child should be collected. Explain over the telephone your concern about the child, for instance, that she has a high temperature or that she has vomited twice.

In general, parents need to know when there are cases of infectious diseases in a centre. Then they will know to watch for the rash or other symptoms in their child. The head of your centre will probably put up a notice explaining that there has been a case of measles – or several cases – in the centre. Such a notice would not name individual children who are ill.

- Special risks

Some illnesses will pose special risks to adults – parents or workers. Pregnant women who have not been inoculated against German Measles (*rubella*) may choose to keep away if there is an outbreak, since this illness can cause severe damage to a foetus in the early months of pregnancy. Men who catch Mumps have the risk, although slight, of inflammation of the testicles and subsequent sterility.

- Confidentiality

You may not be informed that some children have a special health condition. For example, the identity of children who have been diagnosed as HIV positive – the condition prior to developing AIDS – is usually kept confidential. The rationale for this secrecy has been that the anxiety felt by parents and sometimes also by workers is out of proportion to the negligible risk of infection through normal care.

Head lice and threadworms

At some point, you will encounter these unpleasant parasites – whether you work in a centre or a family home. Lice and worms spread easily, especially in groups of children, even when you are careful over hygiene.

A general notice would be put up or a letter sent out if any child is found to have head lice. The wording would be something like: 'There has been a case of head lice in the centre. We suggest that you check your child'. There would be no mention of the child's name except, of course, to her own parents.

ACTIVITY

Ask at your local clinic or chemist for leaflets about head lice or worms. Read them so that you know the current advice. Date and keep the leaflet in your work file. Lice become resistant to the special shampoos available, so the suggested treatment will change with time.

ACTIVITY

Choose one of the organisations listed in Appendix 2, part B. Contact the organisation by telephone and explain that you are undertaking a small project on the special care needed, for example, by children who have epilepsy (The British Epilepsy Association). Ask to be sent their basic literature – they will tell you if you should send a stamped addressed envelope.

Read the material that you are sent and make notes on how you could put the suggestions into practice in your centre if you were caring for a child with this condition.

Children recovering from an illness need to play

ACTIVITY

Find out from your supervisor or a health visitor about those illnesses which must be notified to the local health services – for example, Scarlet Fever.

4.3 Children at risk

Most families treat their children with care and concern. Yet some children are ill-treated by the very people who should be protecting them – their parents or other relatives, or by carers who are taking temporary responsibility.

What is abuse?

You should be aware that there can be different patterns of abuse inflicted on children:

- Physical abuse involves the deliberate harming of a child by physical attack or ill treatment. Examples of physical abuse would be a father who injured his daughter by shaking her violently or a mother who deliberately burned her son with a cigarette end.

- Sexual abuse is the term used to describe inappropriate, intimate physical contact with a child. Such abuse does not necessarily involve forcing full sexual intercourse on a child. For example, it would be abusive for a teenage boy to persist in sexually fondling his young cousin or making her touch his private parts.

- Emotional abuse of children occurs when they are continually ignored, ridiculed or insulted. Such treatment destroys children's sense of self worth and can affect their state of health even when there is no physical attack.

- Neglect would be described as a form of abuse if parents or other carers *deliberately* failed to meet children's basic physical needs. Sometimes one child within a family is seriously neglected in contrast with other siblings. For example, a boy may be noticeably more poorly dressed than his brother or sister and perhaps he is excluded from treats.

Why does it happen?

There may be a number of reasons that seem to explain the behaviour of adults or young people who abuse children. These people may be under extreme stress or they may themselves have been victims of abusive treatment. Whatever the reasons for the abuser's behaviour, the children being abused must be protected.

What should you look out for?

You should be concerned about any of the following:

- Bruises, cuts or burns on a child that a parent cannot satisfactorily explain and to your knowledge the injury has not resulted from an accident at the centre.

- Repeated incidents when a child is injured and explanations are vague or unconvincing.

- Children who are regularly hungry, smelly or inappropriately dressed for the weather. Action would depend on what is known about the financial situation of the family.

- Children who, by words or actions, show a sexual awareness unusual for their age.

- Children whose behaviour has noticeably changed in the time that you have known them. For example, a child who has become very aggressive towards the other children or a previously outgoing child who has become very withdrawn.

What should you do?

Consult before taking any further action

- You should listen to children who want to tell you that something has happened to upset them. However, you shouldn't press them to go any further than they want to nor should you question a child whose behaviour you find disturbing.
- You should discuss your observations and your concerns with your supervisor, and should certainly consult him or her before asking parents for an explanation.
- Within the same day you should make notes of your conversation with a child or of the behaviour that has concerned you.

Don't jump to conclusions

You shouldn't ignore any of the situations just described, yet you can't usually treat a single incident as evidence of abuse. In consultation with your supervisor you should be looking at patterns of behaviour or events.

You should also be ready to consider explanations that do not include abuse. For instance:

- parents may be reluctant to explain because they fear that you will not believe them;
- children infected with threadworms scratch themselves and can become red and sore around the anus;
- dark skinned children often have differences in skin pigmentation on their body that can look like bruises.

Children who are neglected are not necessarily being deliberately abused by their parents:

- a very young mother or father without any family support may be ignorant of even the most basic needs of children for food and warmth and care;
- parents with serious financial worries and poor accommodation may be unable to care well for their children, and these may be the reasons why the children are hungry or their clothes are rarely washed.

Such parents will need support and any practical help that the centre can offer.

Taking children seriously

There is a difference between 'taking a child seriously' who tells you that somebody is hurting her and 'believing' exactly what she tells you, without further corroboration.

These two have sometimes been confused in the upsetting subject of child abuse. The example of Annie and Peter in the box illustrates the difference with a non-abusive situation that often arises among children.

ACTIVITY

Find out from your supervisor how you are expected to behave if you see worrying physical or behavioural signs from children. Make notes in your work file.

ANNIE AND PETER

Imagine that 4 year old Annie comes to you and says, 'Peter hit me but I hadn't done anything!' It would be very unjust if you immediately took Annie's word as the whole truth of what had happened.

A fair approach would be to listen to what Annie tells you and show that you take her upset seriously. You aren't brushing her feelings to one side or telling her she must be mistaken.

Then you would find out Peter's side to the event and perhaps talk with another child who had also been present. You would come to a conclusion on the basis of all the information you could gather.

So you are taking what Annie said seriously but you aren't believing her version of events without checking.

4.4 Well-being of workers

You will become skilled in doing more than one thing at a time

The importance of a positive outlook

Caring requires a lot of physical activity and emotional energy. Young children demand that you react quickly and adjust to changes of direction in their interests. You will need to cultivate the skill of doing, or keeping track of, several things at the same time. For example, you may be changing a toddler's nappy, while chatting with an older child who is interested in what you are doing.

Two points are especially important:

- Focus on what you have achieved

A good worker encourages children and alerts them to what they have learned. You need to give yourself the same attention. Your supervisor should support you by pointing out how you have helped the children – especially if you are tending to dwell gloomily on what you haven't managed.

- Let annoyances go

Your work will not go smoothly all the time. A bad day will only get worse if you chew over frustrations and dwell on imagined slights. You need to take what action is possible and then start afresh. Your supervisor may be able to suggest a way to carry on after an argument with a parent or to take a different approach to a child whom you are finding difficult.

Keeping healthy

Your centre should meet standards of health and safety and you are responsible for following guidelines. However, you must be the one to take personal care of your own health and well-being.

Catching infections

You will come into close contact with many children and adults. You are therefore liable to catch illnesses, especially in your first years of working with young children. Some workers find that they develop some resistance to common illnesses. Do your best to take care of yourself with a healthy diet and by taking exercise.

Bend at the knees to adjust to a child's height

Straining your back

Minor back injuries are a common hazard in working with young children. It is important that you bend at the knees, rather than from the waist, to pick up children or to shift equipment. Facilities for changing babies and toddlers need to be at a comfortable height for you as well as being safe for the children. It is surprising how quickly you will feel an ache in your back if you have to bend over at a low angle.

If you are pregnant

In this event, discuss with your supervisor how your pattern of work might be adjusted. You will still be able to do much of the job, but it would be wiser to let a co-worker carry heavier equipment or lead the more vigorous games with the children.

Leave work behind

When days have gone particularly well you will feel a glow of satisfaction and enjoyment. On days that children have stretched your patience to the limits you may feel as if your reserves have been drained.

You need to be able to leave your job behind at the end of your working day. You may find this more difficult to do if the children with whom you work have unhappy or deprived lives. As hard as it can be, you need, with the help of your supervisor to focus on what you can do to help children or their parents. Many aspects of children's lives are out of your control – and who is to say that you would make the best decision if you did have that responsibility?

Sadness when children move on

Part of caring about children as individuals is a sense of loss when they leave you. You may be excited for them and sad for yourself. It is acceptable to have these feelings, although you must realise that such changes are part of your work. It should be possible to talk over how you feel with another worker or your supervisor.

Personal satisfaction in your job

Caring well for babies and young children is hard work. Only people who spend little or no time with them believe that it's one of the easier ways to earn a living. Experienced workers will tell you that, despite the challenges of the job and often because of them, caring can be a source of great satisfaction and enjoyment. Close personal contact is part of the job and you have the opportunity to see your efforts contributing to children's development.

TO THINK ABOUT

What helps you, personally, to relax at the end of a hard day? Make a list of simple and cheap ideas that cheer you up.

ACTIVITY

Complete the following sentence to help you explore situations at work that you find especially difficult to leave behind:

'I keep thinking about my working day in the evening when...'

Take turns with a partner to listen to each other. What kind of events do you continue to think over? Are these worrying or do you both enjoy thinking about days that have gone well? Do each of you have the opportunity to discuss concerns with your supervisor?

5 Development from birth to 8 years

In this chapter we will explain what is meant by child development and describe the ways in which children change as they develop from birth to their eighth birthday.

5.1 How children develop

All children develop within a particular society and cultural tradition. Their experiences will be shaped by the activities that are offered to them by adults and by the opportunities and the limitations of the environment in which they live.

In what ways do children develop?

The differences between a young baby and a 7-year-old are striking even to people who have limited experience of young children. The many changes that occur in between these years can be less obvious.

Learning new skills

Working with young children is especially exciting because you are able to watch and help as they learn to *do* something new. For example, three weeks ago 13-month-old Susie was crawling around the floor of the centre. Two weeks ago she took her first teetering steps. Now she is walking more than crawling, and the delight shows on her face. Her new skill enables Susie to play differently since she can now move about and still have her hands available for holding toys.

Learning concepts

Your work will be more satisfying as you realise that you have helped a child to *understand* something new. For example, you will find out that 4-year-old Marius believes that you live at the centre when he asks, 'Where's your bed?' You may think that explaining about your home is rather mundane – yet it is of great interest to Marius who then asks you more questions about how you get to work and 'Does your Daddy drive you?'

Observing and assessing development

You can describe children through their abilities and outlook in several different areas of development. For example:

- children will be progressing in physical skills;

41

- at the same time they will be learning to communicate in some way, even if they haven't yet learned to talk;
- children will be applying several different skills as they become more self reliant in their own care;
- children will also be learning about their environment – their discoveries and new concepts will affect how they play;
- babies and children will be forming relationships with adults and with each other.

It's important that you know how the children in your care are developing. This knowledge will support how you help children learn through play and their contact with you. You should also notice if a child doesn't appear to be progressing in one or more areas of development.

Babies and children are developing in the different areas simultaneously. A careful assessment of an individual child has to cover all the aspects of development. In your work you might be asked to write a short report on a child under separate headings. Example A in the box below shows the beginning of this kind of report.

EXAMPLE A

David Wadsworth: 2 years and 5 months
Report by Hasina, 22 March 1993.

Language
I made a list of the words that David uses – 150.
He says short sentences – up to 5 or 6 words. I can understand most of what David says. This week he has started to make 'jokes' – he says something he knows isn't true, e.g. 'Hasina – you a boy!', and then laughs.

Ability to care for self
David wears pants for the daytime. He has some accidents if I don't remind him to go to the toilet – twice this week. Mrs Wadsworth says David wears a nappy at night. David can feed himself with a spoon and fork.

Play
David likes playing with water and play dough. He plays 'coming to tea' with the figures in the dolls house. David has started to chalk and draw with wax crayons. He can climb the indoor frame and runs at speed.

And so on...

Alternatively you may be asked to complete an assessment by ticking what a child can do and adding brief comments. Example B in the box below shows how such a report might start.

ACTIVITY

With your supervisor look at the form or record used in the centre for making an assessment of a child's development. Complete a form, or part of one, for one child and discuss what you have written with your supervisor.

EXAMPLE B

Melanie Sayers: 4 years and 1 month
Completed by Lawrence during week of 17–21 May 1993.

Fine coordination

Copy a vertical line	☑	very wobbly
Turn pages of book one by one	☑	sometimes
Thread large beads onto lace	☑	one or two
Pour water from jug	☑	spills a lot
Build tower of 10 or more bricks	☑	10
Copy a horizontal line	☑	very wobbly
Cut 5 cm strip of paper	No	

Summary

Melanie seems to find it hard to attend – she didn't look carefully at what I was showing her, and often looked away when she was building or pouring. Melanie had most difficulty with using a pencil to make lines or shapes. Suggested activities at the end of the assessment.

5.2 Social and emotional development

Making contact

Even young babies are aware of other people around them – adults and other children. They will show an interest and a desire for attention. You should be concerned by a baby of even a few months old who does not seem to react – by looking and smiling – to what should be familiar faces.

Making friends

Children sometimes enjoy playing alone and at other times they want the company of adults or other children. Children will not get along with all other children of a similar age. For example, even children under 2 may try to avoid a child whose pattern of play is very aggressive.

Children may play happily together or alongside each other

Boys and girls under 5 are likely to play together – unless any of them have learned to reject the opposite sex because of what other children or parents have said. You may notice that 6- or 7-year-olds are beginning to form single sex groups, although some boys and girls will still be playing and talking together.

Acceptance or rejection

You would usually leave children to make their friends as they please. You should definitely help out under two conditions:

1. If you notice that a particular child appears to be having difficulty in making friends.

Talk with your supervisor about a possible approach – since you don't want to make things worse. If you are involved in play activities you may be able to ease a child into a group and show him how to play if he is unused to other children.

ACTIVITY

Watch a baby who is 5 or 6 months old. How does she get the attention of adults or children? For example, does she call out or reach out for someone who is near?

Make a note to remind yourself of how even very young children are active in relationships with other people.

ACTIVITY

Are you working with a child who seems to have difficulty in making friends?

Watch this child and observe how he behaves with other children of a similar age. For example, does he grab toys whereas the other children have learned to ask or wait? Make notes on what you have noticed and talk with another worker. Write down two ideas on how you could help.

2. If any child seems to be rejected consistently by other children – especially if you hear children making rude comments about the child's race, sex or any disabilities.

You should tell a child who makes such a remark that her words are unkind, but make sure that this child realises that you are cross about what she said; you are not rejecting her. You should take opportunities within play and in the books that you look at with the children to emphasise positive images.

Children's feelings about themselves

You will be able to see how children flourish when their efforts are welcomed. They grow in confidence when their mistakes are treated as an opportunity for learning.

When they receive a great deal of encouragement, then children can accept your suggestions on how they might do something differently and not feel that you are saying their way was wrong. In contrast, children who are usually criticised become disheartened and may give up trying altogether.

Children need to feel valued and that they belong. You can support them in developing a sense of pride that doesn't depend on belittling other children.

5.3 Physical development

Physical abilities

At the beginning

Newborn babies are unable to take any deliberate control over their physical movements. They are born with reflex actions such as sucking and grasping, although very premature babies may not make all the reflex actions.

From the early months of a baby's life you will see her making the effort to use her existing strength and ability. She manages to turn to look for the source of an interesting noise or to grab hold of an intriguing toy. Her success in these simple movements brings her into contact with more sights and sensations. She is then motivated to do more.

Learning the skills of mobility

Most children learn an impressive array of physical skills during the years from birth to their eighth birthday.

Within the first year of life babies are gaining control of the muscles in their bodies. They become able to turn and reach out, to grab and then to explore objects of interest. They also learn to move themselves around by rolling, crawling and then by walking. In the second year of life toddlers become confident walkers and increase their speed – by starting to run.

Once they no longer have to concentrate totally on the task of walking without falling over, young children are able to combine the skill with another activity. For example, they may enjoy pushing along a toy wheelbarrow.

Some 2- and 3-year-olds learn to control push along bikes and then tricycles. The play of 3- and 4-year-olds often uses their ability to run at speed, jump, hop and climb. They become more accurate in throwing, catching and kicking balls.

Children of 4–5 years have an array of physical skills which could be applied in a wide range of activities. A great deal depends on what is available. For example, some 5-year-olds who have been taken regularly to the swimming pool will be able to swim. Those 6-year-olds who have the space to practise safely on their bikes will be confident riders. In the few ice rinks around the country you will see 5- and 6-year-olds who are good skaters.

First steps will be as exciting for you as for her

ACTIVITY

Choose one 4- or 5-year-old child whom you know well.
Make a list of this child's physical skills.
Make a note also of skills that this child has nearly achieved.
   Lay out your notes like this:

Shaun, aged 4
Shaun can climb to the top of the centre climbing frame.
He kicks the football but often misses.

And so on...

Young children can take great care in their work

Learning to coordinate physical movements

Children also learn to coordinate what they see and feel with their ability to control their feet, hands and fingers.

Young babies need all their concentration to hit a dangling toy held in front of them. Yet by 9 months they are able to see an object of interest, reach out and successfully grasp it – unless it's very small – and then explore the object before dropping it and watching as it falls to the ground.

Toddlers enjoy arranging and rearranging toys in their play. They are able to search out and use even small objects and are fond of putting small objects into larger containers, tipping everything out and then starting again. Toddlers will reach for any interesting object, so adults have to keep them safe.

Toddlers will start to draw with thick crayons and to paint if they are given the opportunity. By 3 and 4 years they can be producing a range of different artwork and enjoying experimenting with colour and texture.

Children will also use their ability to coordinate their physical skills as they learn to feed themselves, complete some of their dressing and take responsibility for keeping themselves clean. Section 7.3 provides more details on how children become self reliant.

Children of 4–5 years can be confident in handling a range of craft materials. They can produce paintings and drawings that are recognisable as showing people or buildings. Some 5- and 6-year-olds will apply the skills they have achieved and learn to write. Children of 7 years can be producing creative writing that they have planned as well as undertaken independently.

5.4 Communicating and learning

Learning language

Babies

Young babies can only communicate their needs by crying. A crying baby is telling you that she is unhappy for some reason, but it is not always easy to identify the reason.

Happy babies make sounds as well. Very young babies may make soft, contented sounds when they are feeding or cuddled to you. As the months pass, babies become able to make a wider range of sounds and, by 6 months, they enjoy making strings of sounds and copying you.

Talking and understanding

Between 1 and 2 years, many toddlers are learning to communicate through words, supported by gestures, to show you what they want. They understand many simple requests from familiar adults. They depend on both your words and your gestures.

Children of 3 and 4 years understand much more of what is said to them. They are also more able to express themselves so that familiar adults and children can understand them. They will have many words which they combine in short sentences and can hold a short conversational exchange with an adult.

By 5–6 years children are able to make their language work for them in different and sophisticated ways. For example:

- they may tell you in detail about what they did at the weekend;
- they may use their verbal skills to tell you how unfair they believe that you've been over some dispute in the centre;
- they may be able to explain why they like their favourite book – they are using language to express and explain an opinion.

Young children depend a great deal on your gestures while they don't understand a lot of the words you use. However, even 5- and 6-year-olds can fail to understand you, if you are talking about an unfamiliar concept or something else outside their experience. You will help by applying the suggestions in section 3.2. Look back at them after you have read this section.

Extra help

Limited communication

If you are working with children who don't appear to make the effort to communicate, then you need to work out what is getting in the way. There could be a number of possible blocks:

- The adults responsible for the children up to now have rarely talked with the children or listened to their efforts to communicate. You will need to provide this experience.
- Children have given up trying in a noisy atmosphere or because they are always interrupted. You will need to provide experience in a quiet situation, preferably one to one.

● Children have a disability that affects communication – perhaps hearing loss. You will need to share your observations about a child with her parents. With their agreement your supervisor might suggest a specialist who could make an assessment and suggest how to help.

Bilingual children

In some bilingual families young children will be learning two languages at the same time. Other children learn a second language after becoming able to speak their first. Children under 8 can and do become successfully bilingual.

You can help by adjusting your language to match the level of a child's understanding. A 4- or 5-year-old who is learning a second language is not short of ideas – she just can't yet express them in this language. She needs you to speak in shorter sentences and make a clear link between what you're saying and the activity or the book that you can both see. She'll also appreciate your learning some phrases from her first language.

You should make sure that all languages spoken by children in your care are equally respected. Even if every child speaks the same language, don't allow them to make fun of unfamiliar ones.

Learning to attend

Children need to learn to listen and look with care. It's not very effective just to tell children they ought to listen. Young children are far more likely to copy what you do. Follow the suggestions about listening in Chapter 3 and you will help children to attend. You need to remember that children will benefit from slightly different help depending on their age. Some brief examples follow:

● You hold the attention of babies by offering variety in play and sound making, and by focusing on what has caught their interest.

1¼ years   3½ years   5¾ years

As well as drawing skills, these sketches show how Tanith's attention span lengthened as she became older

● Toddlers can become very absorbed and will concentrate so hard on one activity that they may ignore everything else. You will help by joining in their play and making sure you have their full attention before you speak or start to show something.

● Children of 3–4 years are more aware of what is going on beyond their immediate play activity and can be easily distracted by noises or jostling children. You will help by directing their attention back to their play after an interruption.

ACTIVITY

If you are working with children who are learning more than one language, talk with your supervisor about how you might best arrange to give extra time to them.

Make a list of activities that these children enjoy and which would provide an opportunity for simple conversations.

● By 5–6 years children are more able to take in suggestions and even to get involved once more after an interruption. Make sure that the atmosphere is calm and fairly quiet.

Making sense of the world

Learning to think

If you watch carefully you will see that even toddlers are trying to make sense of the world about them. They become aware of routines and are able to predict something about how a familiar adult or child is likely to react.

FOR EXAMPLE

Angus, who is 3 years old, has developed a game with his 13-month-old sister which follows a similar pattern each time. Angus builds a tower of bricks as Tessa watches. She waits for him to say the words, 'What about this, Tessa?' and then she knocks them down. They both laugh loudly and then Angus starts to build again.

Some days, if Angus does not start the game, Tessa fetches the box of bricks and hands it to him. Her expectant look shows that she has remembered the game and is taking the initiative to play it again.

Abstract concepts

When children start to talk they learn the words for naming concrete objects like 'cup' and the names of familiar people in their life. By 3 years children know a considerable number of words to name objects and they are now learning to use their language to distinguish between objects with the same name.

Words like 'big' or 'little' are descriptions that don't make any sense unless they are applied to concrete objects. So when a 3-year-old tells you that he has a 'big cup' he is showing that he has started to learn abstract concepts. Children have made a leap in their development when they can reliably pick you a car that is blue or the tallest child.

Suppose several children complain to you that Jodie has more than her fair share of the building bricks. They are showing that they have understood the concept of sharing. They are also showing their expectation that you will help.

ACTIVITY

During one week in your centre, watch out for examples of the following two ways in which 3- and 4-year-olds show you that they are *thinking*:

● Do the children come to you with problems or complaints and wait as if they expect you to do something?
● Do you hear children using words that describe abstract concepts?

Make notes of your observations in this way:

Monday 29th November 1993
1. **Sharing and expectations about my behaviour**
Dolan and Sophie complained to me that Nathan wouldn't let go of the red bike. They stood and waited until I went over to Nathan.
2. **Relative speed**
Lauretta and Christopher were playing with the cars. They were pushing each car hard and saying 'mine went faster than yours'.

5.5 Special concerns

Uneven patterns of development

Babies and children don't develop in a smooth uninterrupted forward pattern. Children use their existing skills as well as learning new ones, and practising is a very important part of normal development. Sometimes children struggle to achieve a particular skill and may need some help from you.

You shouldn't be anxious about children unless they seem to be noticeably late in some aspect of their development or the pattern of development is very uneven. You can only make this kind of judgement from a knowledge of how children of the same age would usually be developing. You should consult your supervisor if you are worried about a child.

Learning difficulties

Some children have a specific learning difficulty which will mean that they need special help in one area of their development.

Dyslexia is an example of a learning difficulty. If you work in a primary school, you will be helping children to read and to write. You may notice that a child continues to have problems with writing his name or with reading very simple phrases, although he has been trying his best for months. Persistent learning difficulties won't improve without special help. Talk with your supervisor and with the child's parents.

Disabilities and development

Children whose development is affected by a disability or health condition will be like fully abled children in many ways. For example:

- children with persistent ill health still get bored if they don't have interesting play activities;
- children with physical disabilities still argue with their friends and will try to talk you out of keeping to the rules;
- children with mental disabilities have feelings and will be hurt by unkind or dismissive treatment.

Children with disabilities may develop more slowly throughout their childhood. Alternatively, a physical or mental disability may mean that a child's development will always be limited in one or more directions. You may have to be more alert to the small changes and steps which are a real achievement for this child and her family.

The impact of any disability on a child's life can be wider than the specific disabling condition. For example, a child's difficulties in moving about or in learning to talk can, in turn, affect how he is able to relate to other children and to join in play. Children with disabilities will need special help and appropriate equipment.

If you are supporting a child with disabilities in your centre, remember that her parents will have to meet her needs along with all the other demands of family life, including any other children. Her parents will have had to adjust emotionally to having a disabled child. Some experts have described this experience as similar to bereavement.

ACTIVITY

Ask your supervisor to describe the special arrangements that were made to support a child with disabilities who is attending the centre.

Make notes on the following points:

- Did the centre obtain any special equipment?
- In what way did workers prepare the other children for the arrival of this child?
- In what way have staff adjusted how they talk or play in order to meet this child's special needs?

Continuing to learn about development

You are at the beginning of your career in working with children. Child development is a very large topic and this chapter has covered only a small part of all the information that is available on how children develop and the many differences between individual children. Be ready to continue to learn by observing children in your care and by talking to experienced workers. You will find that there is always more to discover and you will experience the excitement and satisfaction of helping children as they develop in all their possible skills.

6 Daily care of babies and young children

This chapter deals with:

● how you can meet the physical needs of babies and children younger than 2 years old in feeding, cleaning and changing;

● how you can meet the emotional needs of babies and toddlers for communication and play while you care for them.

6.1 Caring and comforting

Social and physical needs

Babies are fully dependent on others to keep them safe and healthy. They need responsible physical care but, in order to thrive, babies also need social contact and affection.

Comfort

● Cuddling and holding

Babies are often calmed by a close cuddle. They are especially reassured by the steady thump of a heartbeat. It's not really surprising that babies are at ease with the sounds of an adult body; they have after all spent about nine months surrounded by this noise.

● Sucking

Babies enjoy sucking at the breast or a bottle. However they also learn to comfort themselves by sucking.

Some babies learn to suck a thumb or fingers. Others seem to be happier with a soother (also called a dummy). Soothers should be kept very clean – some can be sterilised. Never dip soothers in juice or other sweet drinks and never let babies suck on bottles of drink as a comforter.

Toddlers will not communicate clearly with a thumb or soother in their mouth. Gently pull it out when you are chatting together.

● Cuddlies

Some children become very attached to a particular teddy, a blanket or even a piece of cloth. A toddler or child may need to hold on tight to his cuddly as he settles into a new situation and accepts a new carer.

You must support young babies' heads

53

Crying

The only way that babies can communicate their need for attention is by crying. Some babies are noisier than others but a continuously quiet baby should concern you.

Your task is to try to work out why the baby is crying this time. The main possibilities are:

- She's hungry.
- He may have a wet or soiled nappy – babies are more likely to cry if they are sore. This is likely if they have developed nappy rash.
- She's in pain – babies do seem to get stomach pains on occasion. Sometimes, they will have swallowed air with their milk. If you hold a baby upright and rub her back very gently, she will burp it up. Some babies apparently get more painful stomach aches, sometimes called colic. Under these conditions they can be very hard to comfort. The baby's parents should consult a doctor if the pains seem severe and definitely if the baby has other symptoms such as vomiting or diarrhoea.
- He's bored – babies like company. If you have gone through all the physical possibilities and a baby is still crying, he probably wants to be cuddled and entertained. Chapter 8 deals with play activities for babies as well as older children.

Sharing care of babies and toddlers

Being a parent

First time parents may lack confidence – however certain they may feel in other parts of their life. Do recognise that parents can be very tired, especially mothers who are most likely to be the ones getting up to feed babies at night.

Many women feel close to tears in the early days after birth. However, some women suffer from post-natal depression – a state far worse than just feeling upset and exhausted. Talk to your supervisor if you become concerned that a mother may be suffering from post-natal depression. The mother will need to be encouraged to consult her doctor.

A consistent routine

You need to pay special attention to keeping to a baby's routine and making sure that care is consistent between adults. Any worries about the baby's well-being should be shared because infections and stomach upsets can take hold of babies very quickly.

Young babies should be cared for consistently by the same one or two workers in a centre. You should have as careful a conversation at the handover with a worker as you would with a parent at the beginning and end of a day.

Respecting the views of parents

You should not impose your own methods of baby care on parents. You may need to reach workable compromises on such issues as picking up crying babies or whether or not the baby has a soother. Make time for a discussion with parents when particular changes are about to occur. For example:

- to understand parents' preferences on diet when a baby moves to mixed feeding;
- to be consistent on timing and approach to toilet training when their toddlers are looking ready for this change.

ACTIVITY

Observe the young children in your care and talk with parents to discover the different things that have been a source of comfort to babies and young children.

Make a note in your work file to remind you of the variety of cuddlies important to young children.

Babies will burp if they need to – hold them like this

ACTIVITY

List three points of information about your care of a baby that you should share with the parent when handing over at the end of the day.

Discuss what you have written with your supervisor.

6.2 Feeding

The needs of young babies

A routine for feeding

Babies under 3 months should be entirely fed on milk, either breast milk or an appropriate formula for bottle feeding. Their digestive systems cannot absorb anything else.

Babies should be fed on demand, that is, when they wake and cry. Newborn babies will need to be fed approximately every 3 to 4 hours, day and night. It can be anything from a few weeks to many months before babies will sleep through the night.

Feeding young babies is part of a routine that also includes changing their nappies and their clothes if they are wet or soiled. It's probably better to feed a baby as soon as she wakes. She can become desperately hungry in the time it takes to change her and then she could be so distressed that she will not suck properly. A second practical point is that sucking often seems to lead to activity at the other end of the body! Then you will only end up changing her again.

Breast feeding

Human babies are designed to be breast fed. The milk emerges at the correct strength and the right temperature. The milk is not only free of germs but also passes important antibodies to a newborn baby. A breast fed baby is held close to a familiar body and is at the best distance for her to focus on her mother's face. For all that it's natural, breast feeding can take from a few days to a couple of weeks to establish with comfort and confidence.

Some women are able to express breast milk which is then stored in bottles. You can give the milk to the baby when the mother is absent. You should follow the same hygienic precautions over stored breast milk as with formula milk.

Bottle feeding

Babies also thrive on bottle feeding. There may be a number of practical reasons why mothers decide to bottle feed or to switch over after a period of breast feeding. If women return to work they may find that breast feeding is no longer possible. Some women find that breast feeding continues to be uncomfortable and they feel more relaxed with bottle feeding.

There are very few medical circumstances in which women would be dissuaded from breast feeding. Women who have been diagnosed as HIV positive or who have developed AIDS are definitely advised not to breast feed, as babies could be infected through the milk.

Hygiene and bottle feeding

● Making up feeds
You must follow *exactly* the instructions for making up any formula milk. Babies who are still hungry after finishing a bottle should be given further quantities of correctly made up milk. At 3 months a demand for more milk may be a sign that the baby is ready for the introduction of mixed feeding.

Bacteria can multiply fast in milk. Any milk left in a bottle when a baby has drunk his fill should be thrown away. It should never be kept for the next feed.

ACTIVITY

Contact the nearest branch of the National Childbirth Trust and make an appointment to talk to a member who could give you information about breast feeding.

If you can't find the Trust in your local telephone directory then contact head office at Alexandra House, Oldham Terrace, London W3 6NH (tel: 081–992–8637).

Find out about common problems in establishing breast feeding and ask the NCT member for advice on how best to offer support and encouragement. Make notes in your file.

Some babies are allergic to cow's milk and can become very ill. Families following a vegan diet will not want their babies to take any dairy products, including cow's milk. Soya formula should then be used.

● Sterilising equipment

All the bottles and teats used for feeding must be thoroughly sterilised. It is not enough to wash them in the same way as cups and dishes. The bacteria which may be left on unsterilised equipment can cause serious stomach upsets, which can be very dangerous for babies.

There are two basic options:

1. The chemical method which uses a sterilising solution.
2. Steam sterilisers which operate by using heat. If you use the kind that works in a microwave, you have to be sure that all of the feeding equipment that you want to sterilise is microwave-safe.

You must follow the instructions exactly for both methods.

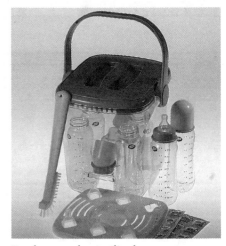

Bottles must be sterilised

Feeding time

When you are bottle feeding a baby, give her all your attention. Hold her comfortably in your arms, close to you. You should *never* prop babies up and leave a bottle in their mouth; always hold the baby and the bottle. Take your time and let her take her time as well.

You don't have to shoo older children away; they are often very interested. You can explain that they must be peaceful or else they may distract the baby from feeding.

Mixed feeding

Between 3 and 4 months of age, a baby will finish his bottle and yet still want to continue sucking. He may cry for food after a shorter interval between feeds than has been usual for him. These are signs that the baby is ready to take in more than just milk.

Consult parents

Find out about the diet of a baby's family. Are there foods that parents don't want given to their children? Also check whether there is any reason to expect the baby to be allergic to any foods or ingredients like gluten.

First foods

The first new foods are extras, not desperately needed meals, so you can be relaxed about introducing them.

● Rice cereal

Start with bought baby rice cereal, which can be mixed with formula milk or expressed breast milk. Babies need a fairly liquid consistency. Offer a small amount on a plastic spoon.

Wheat-based cereals are not recommended for babies until they reach about 6 months.

Neither baby rice nor any other kind of cereal should ever be mixed into a baby's bottle of milk. Such a practice forces babies to take in more cereal than they may need or can easily digest in order to drink the milk they definitely do need.

● First fruit and vegetables

After introducing rice cereal you can try ripe apples or pears which have been cooked and pureed. Banana mashes well and doesn't need cooking. You can also try cooked, pureed root vegetables like potato or carrot.

ACTIVITY

Make notes on appropriate first foods for a baby from a vegetarian family. You can add to your own ideas by:

1. Discussions with a health visitor – see later activity.
2. Contacting the Vegetarian Society at Parkdale, Dunham Road, Altrincham, Cheshire, WA14 4QG (tel: 061–928–0793). The Society publishes leaflets on infant feeding.

ACTIVITY

Make an appointment to talk to a local health visitor:

1. Does the health visitor have suggestions about bottle feeding, for example, what to do if a baby does not seem to digest one brand of milk very well?
2. Ask for advice about introducing babies to mixed feeding and add the details to your work file.

● At 5–6 months you can introduce other fruits such as mango, peach or melon and vegetables including cauliflowers, spinach or tomato. You can try babies with pulses such as lentils which cook to a soft mushy texture. Avoid the citrus fruits, such as oranges, since they can cause diarrhoea.

● From 6 months try small amounts of mild cheese (very finely grated or mixed with vegetables), yogurt and wheat-based cereals produced for babies. You can also introduce chicken – minced or cut very small – and white fish which has been broken into flakes and carefully checked to remove bones.

Following the salmonella scares of the late 1980s, current advice is to avoid eggs until babies are over 12 months. You should first introduce well cooked egg yolk – not the white of the egg – and make sure that babies can digest the yolk before using whole eggs.

Taking care

Following the pattern already given, you should introduce one new food for a couple of days. If you keep to one new taste at a time and the baby vomits or gets an upset stomach, then you can be fairly sure of the cause. Don't combine foods until you are sure that both are well digested by this baby:

● Don't be surprised if babies take a few tries to get used to a new taste. You should be concerned about symptoms like vomiting, diarrhoea and blotchy rashes, although mild reactions may simply mean that the baby is not yet ready for this food. Consult your supervisor if you are uncertain.

● Any spoons or dishes should be washed up thoroughly, rinsed in clean water and left to drip dry.

● Fresh fruit and vegetables should be peeled and de-seeded where necessary, then boiled in a small amount of water or steamed. Don't add sugar, salt or any other seasonings and don't add butter or other fats to vegetables. If you sieve or liquidise the food you will make a fine puree.

● Never re-use a bought jar of baby food or a container of home-made food in which you have dipped a spoon that has been in the baby's mouth. The saliva left on the spoon starts a breakdown of the food – necessary within the body, but a possible source of harmful bacteria outside.

Using convenience baby foods

You will find a very wide range of commercially produced baby foods. The labels should give advice on the age of the babies for whom the food is designed. Some brands are clearly marked as suitable for babies from vegetarian families. Prepared baby foods are convenient but at least consider making some fresh food for a baby.

Joining in mealtimes

By 8–9 months a baby should have tried enough of a range of foods to be able to start taking tasters of the meals that you provide for older children. Whatever the diet, be cautious about the more highly seasoned meals or richer tasting dishes.

● Make eating easy

Mash the food well since babies will have few if any teeth. Finger foods of finely grated cheese, apple or raw carrot will be an enjoyable addition for a baby. She may like to chew on hard rusks, a piece of toast, or sliced apple and carrot.

- Stay with them

You should never leave babies alone while they are eating, because of the risk of choking.

- Don't expect neatness

Babies eat most effectively with their own clean fingers and a spoon. You can wield a second spoon to help some of the food in. The key is for you to relax, don't push food into a baby's mouth and don't hurry mealtimes.

An enjoyable mealtime for a baby or toddler is very messy in comparison with the meals you can have with older children. You can avoid some of the spillages by giving babies a bowl that will stick to the eating surface and a lidded cup once they abandon a bottle. Even if you put a bib on the baby and an apron on yourself you will still have to clean up afterwards.

He won't be clean for long

Vitamin drops

Totally bottle fed babies should not be given drops, since formula milk has vitamins added. Drops are advised for breast-fed babies after 6 weeks, but you shouldn't give vitamin drops until after a discussion with parents.

Drinks

Babies on mixed feeding can continue to drink formula milk and enjoy breast feeding. You can introduce other drinks:

- Cow's milk

Once babies have happily taken to milk products, such as cheese and yogurt, introduce full milk (silver top) to go on their cereal. By 9–12 months, babies can be drinking cow's milk. Don't use skimmed or semi-skimmed milk for babies or toddlers – there isn't enough nourishment in it.

Some babies remain allergic to cow's milk and should not be given it in any form – nor should it be given to babies whose families follow a vegan diet.

You should still sterilise bottles and anything that could trap bacteria, such as the lid of a drinking beaker, just as carefully as you did for a totally milk fed baby.

- Water

Babies are unlikely to need water unless the weather is hot. Water should be boiled and allowed to cool. Use filtered water if this is usual at your centre – ask your supervisor. Bottled spring water is often not a good idea for babies; some contain higher than average amounts of sodium.

- Fruit juice

There is a bewildering array of baby juice drinks on the market. These are no more essential for babies than the many flavoured milk drinks. If older babies enjoy slightly flavoured water, you can add small amounts of juice – at most two thirds water to one-third juice. Try only small amounts of citrus juice, such as orange or grapefruit.

6.3 Nappies and changing

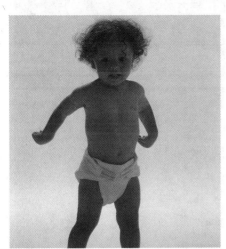

Children will need to be in nappies until at least 18 months

Anyone caring for children under 2 years old will be dealing with a lot of nappies. The earliest that young children are likely to be ready to start toilet training will be 18–24 months. Boys tend on average to be about 6 months later than girls, who are physically more able to gain bladder control.

Attempts to get babies or young toddlers out of nappies simply leads to masses of wet knickers and puddles on the floor. Toilet training is covered in section 7.3.

Nappies

What kind?

The choice of nappies is between the many different kinds of disposable nappies and towelling nappies. Disposables are the most used now, but environmental groups are concerned that they are not easily disposable beyond the first dustbin.

For boys or girls?

You will notice that disposable nappies are sold in boy and girl versions. They vary in where the thickest padding is provided. The urine of boys tends to go into the front part of the nappy, closest to the penis. However, the urine of girls tends to flow to the back of a nappy.

If you use towelling nappies, you need to fold them to give the thickest amount where the urine is likely to collect.

Changing time

A place for changing

- The surface on which you change any baby or toddler should be very clean. Ask your supervisor what kind of disinfectant you should use.
- You should never take your attention off the baby, even to turn around for what seems like a moment to you. A moment has been long enough for older babies to roll and lever themselves off a changing table.
- You should have everything you need close to hand but *not* within the baby's reach. You need a fresh nappy, cotton wool and cream or lotion for cleaning the baby's bottom. You will also need a bag for the used nappy.

It is also wise to put a tissue over a boy baby's penis when his nappy is off. If he urinates whilst uncovered, the urine can travel some distance. Girls' urine will simply trickle onto the changing mat.

Checking on the baby

Changing time is an opportunity to check on the well-being of a baby or toddler. Look carefully to see that he is free of nappy rash or sore skin, especially in the folds of his armpits and the tops of his legs.

You should also take note of any scratches or bruises, but consult your supervisor before asking parents any questions arising from unexplained marks. Section 4.3 describes how to proceed if you are worried that a child is at risk.

The contents of a baby's nappy will also tell you something about his well-being. The stools of a breast-fed baby have a milder, milky smell compared to those resulting from bottle feeding. With the move to mixed feeding, a baby's stools will steadily become more solid and have a stronger smell, depending on what the baby is now eating.

Afterwards

You need to wash your hands or remove disposable gloves when you have changed a baby. She must be safe in a proper baby seat or watched over by another worker while you do this.

Disposable nappies should be bagged before being added to the general rubbish. Towelling nappies have to be soaked in a sterilising solution, then washed before re-use. You will find the appropriate solutions, with clear instructions, in any chemists or shop selling baby equipment and products.

Play and changing time

From the baby's point of view changing time is an opportunity for happy contact and play. You need to be careful that she doesn't put her hands into urine or faeces, but otherwise she can have a nice time.

Not all babies enjoy all aspects of being changed and a tired or unwell baby may complain loudly. However, you and the baby have many changing times to get through and it's in everybody's interest to make the most of the time:

Making the most of changing time

- Young babies may stare at you in interest. You can smile back and talk softly or sing as you change them.
- 3–4-month-old babies may like a rattle to hold. Don't let them play with things like talcum powder, since they could breathe it in if they tip the container.
- Chat with babies and toddlers about what you are doing.

ACTIVITY

With the support of an experienced worker, change a baby's nappy.

Clothes

Choice of clothes

Parents will choose what their babies and toddlers wear. If asked, you can make suggestions about clothes that are easier for play. For example, crawling babies of either sex move more easily in trousers or dungarees.

Dressing and undressing

Young babies cannot help you in their dressing – you must do it all and watch out to make sure that little fingers don't get bent back by mistake. After about 6 months, babies may join in as you dress them. They may push an arm into a sleeve if you hold it out. The activity is playful as far as the baby is concerned, so don't be surprised if she pulls an arm or leg back out again.

Toddlers may cooperate as you help them into or out of their clothes, so long as you don't rush them. They may be able to pull elasticated trousers up the last bit or pull down a sweat shirt. You can encourage them by doing it together.

Toddlers and older children won't always want to cooperate, especially if dressing or undressing means they have to stop an activity they enjoy.

6.4 Sleep and rest

Wakeful periods

Very young babies will sleep for a lot of the time when they aren't feeding and being changed. At 2 to 3 months, babies won't go back to sleep immediately and will need to be entertained. They will get unhappy if you don't play with them and keep them company.

From 6 to 9 months, babies are likely to be in a daily pattern in which activity is broken up with naps. They will sleep for many hours during the night but some will still be waking their parents. Babies' views of an ideal time to start the day's activities are not always shared by adults.

A place to sleep

Babies don't only sleep in cots; they will doze off almost anywhere so long as they are comfortable and feel safe. Some babies need to be rocked before they will settle and some are soothed by being wheeled about in a pram or buggy.

Toddlers often fall asleep in the buggy. Make sure they cannot get chilled while sleeping, especially on autumn and winter days. Remove hats and coats if they are still sleeping when you bring them back indoors, otherwise they can get far too hot.

In group care, both babies and older children should have their own place to sleep (cot, bed or sleeping bag for older children) and their own bedding. Don't use pillows with babies under 12 months.

Cot death

This phrase is used to cover the sudden and unexplained death of a baby – often during sleep. Some 80% of cot deaths happen to babies who are between 1 and 6 months, and winter is the most vulnerable time of the year.

It is important that you follow the most recent guidelines to reduce cot deaths, but you should also know that most babies safely pass through the first year of their life. In 1991, 1134 babies of under a year died of cot death. This is a rate of 1.43 per 1000 live births. These figures are from the 1991 Census and more recent figures from some local health districts are showing an encouraging reduction in cot deaths.

Whether a baby is sleeping in a cot or in a pram, you should follow these recommendations:

- Lie babies on their back or side to sleep and not on their stomachs.
- Keep babies in a smoke-free atmosphere.
- Don't let babies get too hot. Air needs to circulate around them, especially the head. Rooms do not need to be warmer than around 65°F (18°C).
- Contact a **doctor** if you think a baby is unwell, especially if she has a fever or breathing problems. You should also be anxious if she is a lot less active than normal for her, or is taking in or passing out a lot less fluid than usual.

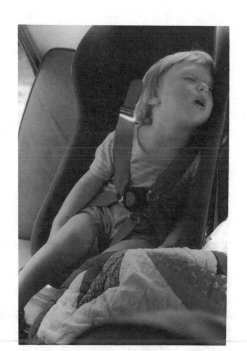

Young children can fall asleep anywhere they feel safe

ACTIVITY

Get a copy of the leaflet *Reduce the risk of cot death* and place it in your file. The leaflet is published by the Foundation for the Study of Infant Deaths (FSID). You may find one in your local clinic or large chemist stores. Alternatively, contact the FSID at 35 Belgrave Square, London SW1X 8QB (tel: 071–235–0965).

6.5 Cleanliness and health

Keeping babies clean

Unlike mobile toddlers, babies don't get grubby. They need to be cleaned gently and thoroughly when they are changed. You also need to wipe and dry around their mouths if they dribble milk or else they may become sore.

Talk with parents about the creams and lotions that are normally used in the centre for baby care. You will notice that most such products are free of fragrances and also lanolin-free since some babies are allergic to this ingredient.

Bathing

Babies often like bathtime and it can be an enjoyable playtime as well as a practical way to wash them. You can also clean babies without putting them into a baby bath. You wash them one half at a time – called 'topping and tailing'.

Like changing time, you need to have everything ready before you start – a warm towel, baby soap or bath lotion and any toy that the baby likes in the bath:

- Babies should be bathed in a warm atmosphere free of draughts. They need water that feels warm – not hot. Test it with your elbow and don't trust the temperature as felt by your hand because your hands are used to hotter water from washing up.

- Let babies enjoy the water. They often relish moving their hands and feet or having you gently dribble water over them. They enjoy splashing.

- Some young babies show a panic reaction when they are first put into a baby bath. You can reassure them by carefully holding them around their shoulders. They will feel safer if you make sure that their feet can feel the end of the bath.

- Babies need to be gently dried after a wash or bath. Pay special attention to the creases in their body, for example, between the legs or under the arms.

- Babies don't need hair washing as such until they have a head of hair rather than soft down. You can wipe the head over gently and use baby shampoo once they have hair.

Skin care

Using creams

Some babies and children will need special care for their skin. For example:

- Babies and children with eczema may have an allergic reaction to ordinary soap. Their parents will tell you what product to use and you should note this in the child's record. Depending on the severity of the condition you may also have to apply special cream during the day.

- Children whose skin easily becomes dry may also need a moisturising cream or lotion. Many dark skinned children need this care on a daily basis. Talk with the child's parents – you may not need to cream an older child unless she has a long day with you or perhaps if you take her swimming.

ACTIVITY

Bath a young baby with an experienced worker at your side for any help if you should need it.

After you have finished, write up notes in your work file. Describe briefly what you did to keep the baby safe and how you helped him play with the water and enjoy bathtime.

Care in a heat wave

Babies should not be allowed to lie or crawl in direct hot sunlight – their skin is especially vulnerable. All children will need some protection against the sun when they are playing outside in hot weather. Pale skinned children will be the first to burn, but dark skinned children will also get sun burn and heat stroke if you don't take care. You should discuss with parents any plans to use sun protection creams on their children, and ask them to send in a sun hat that their child is willing to wear.

In a long hot spell you will have to ration all children's time in direct sun and make sure that they drink plenty of liquids.

Teeth and teething

Cutting teeth

At some point in the first year of life, a baby's first set of teeth will start to emerge. Although teething doesn't always cause a lot of distress, some babies can be in discomfort. They are more likely to be in pain as the molars come through.

Babies often feel better if they can chew against something hard and cool, even cold. Teething rings or clean and safe baby toys can comfort the teething baby. Some babies like to gnaw against a raw carrot or a hard rusk. Don't leave them alone when they are doing this.

Teething babies sometimes dribble more. They need gentle wiping of their chin and chest, so they don't get sore. Very dribbly babies may need a cloth bib, which you change regularly. Don't leave the bib on when they take a nap.

Chemists sell teething gels suitable for babies and young children. These can be rubbed gently on the gums, but consult parents before using such gels.

Teething babies can be miserable. However, it's important that you don't put a whole range of symptoms down to teething. Cutting teeth cannot, for example, cause diarrhoea, fever or vomiting – a cause for serious concern in babies.

Care of teeth

- Brushing

Once babies have teeth, they should be introduced to the habit of tooth cleaning using a soft brush. Some dentists are wary of getting children to clean their teeth after every meal, on the grounds that over-brushing may damage the tooth enamel. So, if you care for babies and children within daytime only, your best contribution to the care of teeth may be to ensure a healthy diet, low on added sugars and without sweets.

- Fluoride

Depending on the level of fluoride in the local water, dentists may recommend fluoride drops to strengthen young children's teeth. You shouldn't give these without parents' permission. Over-dosing with fluoride causes mottling of the teeth. An older child who uses and swallows a fair bit of a fluoride toothpaste may also be getting enough fluoride without taking drops.

The importance of caring

Caring for babies and very young children requires careful attention to their safety and their comfort. A routine will help you to meet their needs and to monitor their well-being, but the routine should never become more important that the babies themselves.

You will have to change babies' nappies many times and feed them at regular intervals. It is important that you also see these times as special opportunities for close physical contact, communication and play. Babies will benefit enormously from this approach, but you will also benefit by finding greater personal satisfaction and enjoyment in your work.

7 Caring for 2- to 8-year olds

This chapter deals with the changing needs of children from 2 to 8 years old in:

- feeding;
- activity and rest;
- help towards taking the responsibility for their own care.

7.1 Meals and mealtimes

A healthy diet

You will be concerned that the children in your care are eating a healthy diet that provides a balanced mix of the different sources of nourishment needed for growth and everyday energy. Unless you are working as a nanny or in a very small centre, you are unlikely to be planning menus or doing the cooking. Your responsibilities are more likely to be as follows:

1. Keeping accurate notes of any dietary requests made by parents.
2. Encouraging children to eat well and drink at snack times and meal-times.

Your ideas about a healthy diet will have been shaped by your own eating habits as well as by the advice that you hear or read. For example:

- if you happily eat meat, you may wonder at first how to achieve a healthy vegetarian diet;
- if you follow Islam or Judaism, you will find it hard to grasp how anybody could eat meat from pigs;
- if you are a vegetarian, you will have trouble understanding how people can eat dead animals at all.

Consulting parents

Parents' beliefs

You need to ask all parents if there are any foods that they do not want you to offer to their children. You need to have a conversation about diet because limited information, such as 'This family is Hindu', will not be enough for you to be sure. For example, some Hindu families are vegetarian but not all. Some Jewish families follow a strictly kosher diet but some may ask only that you don't give their child pork or shellfish.

ACTIVITY

If possible, talk with people whose beliefs lead them to follow a different diet from yours.

How do they make their meals interesting and nutritious without some of the foods that you take for granted?

Start a section in your work file on beliefs and diet.

65

Dislikes and allergies

There may be some foods that parents know their child detests. It would be silly to push these on to the child. If you respect children's serious dislikes, they are more likely to cooperate in trying new foods.

Some children need to avoid certain foods in order to stay well. If they are allergic to a food, even a small amount could make them very ill – producing skin rashes, swellings or vomiting and diarrhoea.

Respect parents' requests

You should note down in a child's records the parents' requests about diet. Talk with your supervisor if you are concerned that it may be difficult for any reason to follow a request. You must be honest with parents if you really cannot fulfil their wishes. Perhaps they can help you maintain a balanced diet for their child by sending in some of their preferred foods or appropriate snacks.

Enjoyable mealtimes

Table manners

We all bring the experience of our own childhood to mealtimes with children, yet the way you were brought up is not the only right way. Different cultures don't share identical rules about how one should eat. For example, everybody in the world doesn't eat with a knife and a fork.

If you share memories with other workers you will find differences in how you were each taught to behave at mealtimes. These memories can affect how we behave now – as adults. For example:

- During childhood perhaps you were allowed to chat at the meal table, whereas others had to be quiet. Are these different experiences leading two workers with a group to give conflicting instructions to the children?

- Perhaps one worker is reluctant to insist that children eat everything up because she believes she sounds just like the fierce dinner lady of her school memories.

You need to work in cooperation with other workers and to find friendly ways to encourage children towards considerate behaviour at the meal table.

Proper meals

You will find it difficult, even impossible, to judge whether a child's diet is balanced unless you have clear mealtimes and snack times.

Children need an intake of food and drink spread through their waking hours. The usual pattern is three clear mealtimes – at the beginning of the day, around mid-day and towards late afternoon or early evening. A lot depends on their age, and children will vary in how much they eat. Many children also welcome a drink and a small snack at mid-morning and mid-afternoon.

Make it friendly

Meal and snack time can be a good opportunity for talking together and you can work to make meals a social time:

ACTIVITY

Summarise your conversation with each parent by making notes in the child's records. Here are two examples of how to write brief notes:

1. Becky is allergic to cow's milk. No cheese, yogurt, milk puddings or custard. Mrs Pierce to bring in the soya milk that Becky drinks at home.
2. Rafat's family do not eat pork. Check that sausages and any tinned meat contain no pork at all.

- Everybody will feel more positive about eating and food if you don't rush. Talk to your supervisor if you are under pressure from kitchen staff to hurry.

- If possible, have meals in serving dishes so that children can see the various ingredients. You can allow them to influence the relative proportions by telling you or serving themselves. Let children add savoury sauces, additions such as chutney or sweet sauces such as custard, only if they want them. You may want to discourage them from adding large amounts.

- It is not worthwhile making a big fuss about children saying 'please' and 'thank you'. If you are courteous in your use of words they will copy you.

- By all means remind children to eat up but don't nag – give them plenty of time before reminding them. Help with the cutting up or spooning if they need it.

- If there is more than one adult (worker or parent) at the meal table, decide who will do the reminding. Children will feel harassed if more than one adult is saying 'Eat up!'

- You will make children feel more involved in food and mealtimes by asking for their opinion about the menus. You need the cooperation of the cook, of course, if you are to act on their suggestions.

- You can teach children to eat neatly and with consideration for the other people at the table and still give them experience of different foods and ways of eating.

- You will teach children most easily by sitting down with them. You may not want to eat something at every meal or snack time, but you should always keep the children company.

7.2 Activity and rest

Daytime naps

Children up to the age of 3 will probably want to sleep at some point during the day. This will most likely be a nap after lunch.

You need to discuss this part of a child's day with parents, just like any other aspect. Some children may appear to need an especially long nap, compared with the others. Parents may be happy for you to let their children sleep longer, perhaps if the family has a very early start to the day. Some parents will want you to wake their child from a nap if the result otherwise is a child full of energy late into the evening.

All children should have a set of bedding for nap time which is not shared with others and is laundered regularly. If sleeping bags have to be dry-cleaned, they must be thoroughly aired before a child uses them for sleeping.

A worker should always be sitting with a group of sleeping children.

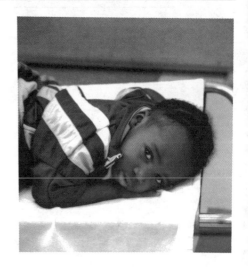

A quiet time

The 3- and 4-year-olds will soon not want a daytime nap. If you have children for a half-day session, your programme of activities will not include nap time. If you have children under 5 for a full day, they will benefit from a quiet time – scheduled when the younger children are actually sleeping.

ACTIVITY

Make a list of activities that the slightly older children might enjoy during quiet time. For instance, what do they ask for during the day that is difficult to do with the younger ones around?

7.3 Encouraging self reliance

Children over 2 years old are physically more *able* to share some of the responsibility for their care, but you will notice also that they often *want* to take part as you dress them or clean them up after mealtimes. Admittedly young children don't always willingly feed themselves or button up their coats, and they won't be as fast as you are.

Helping children to learn

Your work includes enabling children to learn the skills of their own care and to help out in your daily routine with activities such as tidying up.

Time and encouragement

You will help children by being patient as they learn and complimenting them on what they have managed so far. However, you will discourage them if your routine is unrealistic in the amount of time you allow for them to help you lay the table or to wipe their faces after lunch.

Explaining and showing

Children need to understand what they have to do as well as practise their physical skills. Sometimes they make mistakes and need your help. For example:

- Young children sometimes make a watery mess when they help with washing up. They don't understand how far water splashes and flows.
- Children may put on their clothes in the wrong order or put the buttons in the wrong holes. They get upset when they realise something has gone wrong but they can't put it right.

Children need plenty of practice and your patient help if they are to become more confident. You can encourage them by showing them how to complete a task and making sure that nobody makes fun of their mistakes.

Do *children* have the coordination?

Everyday tasks like eating don't come easily. Wielding any utensils for eating will require coordination of eye and hand. Some spills are inevitable as children are learning. You may have to show a child how to take a safer grip on a spoon and how to hold it steady on the journey from the plate to the mouth.

Helping out

Helping children who can cope

Children will be pleased with their ability to meet realistic challenges. However, they will be unhappy if adults put too much pressure on them or make an issue of refusing to help a child with something that she could do for herself.

Children who can do up their own coats or cut their food, still ask for help sometimes. You might well suggest, 'I want you to have a go first'. Then you can give some help as well as complimenting children on what they have done so far. It is very easy to get into a power battle with a child if you refuse to compromise at all.

The impact of disabilities

You need to be especially sensitive to children with physical disabilities that may limit their ability to take on some of their own care. Children of 4–5 years may be uncomfortably aware that their fully abled friends need less help with dressing or going to the toilet.

You can help by taking advantage of any specially adapted equipment, for example, eating utensils. You should also be alert to any changes you could make in your care that would enable a child with disabilities to take over even a small part. Such a change might mean that this part of the routine would take longer, but it would be time well spent if the child feels more competent and involved.

Involving children in the daily routine

Children want to feel involved and they enjoy working alongside adults within the daily routine. They are pleased and flattered when you trust them with a manageable part of a grown up task.

Children will almost certainly take longer than you would and they will fail if you impose unrealistic standards. So, take a look at your domestic routine – whether you are working in a centre or a family home – and see if you are missing opportunities for the children to join in with you and therefore to learn. Some examples are:

- Even toddlers like to feel helpful by handing you something that you need – a tissue, a spoon or a pencil.

- 3- and 4-year-olds can have learned enough to be trusted to take a simple message or to accompany a worker to fetch the meal trolley from the kitchen.

- Let the children help you lay the table and clear up afterwards.

- Children also like to be involved in the care of children younger than themselves. The 3- and 4-year-olds are often fascinated by baby care, and are keen to watch and ask questions.

    Of course, you must remain responsible for the baby's safety yet children can hand you a clean nappy or the tub of cream, and they could choose some clean clothes for the baby. Children are often very good at amusing a baby while you are doing the changing.

- Encourage children to help in tidying up. If you have a simple system for putting toys away, even toddlers can help to put all the bricks back in the brick box.

    A child can help by putting all the bits of a posting box back in. The activity can be satisfying for the child and he might notice for you whether anything has gone missing.

    It's worth your time to organise your helpers and explain which part of a task you want them to undertake. Children deserve a proper 'Thank you' for their efforts afterwards. It's not impossible to make tidy up time an enjoyable part of play activities.

- Look also for any opportunities to allow children over 3 years to make some decisions relevant to your day together. There may be a realistic choice between possible play activities or trips out. Children will feel more involved in the group activities and they will also be using their language skills as they tell you what they would like to do and maybe remember an activity that you all did a couple of weeks previously.

ACTIVITY

Ask your supervisor to help you contact an occupational therapist or physiotherapist. Take notes from your discussion of any suggestions on helping children with disabilities to become more self reliant. Make a note of any books or equipment companies suggested by the therapist.

Clothes

Dressing and undressing

Even the simpler ways of fastening clothes can be difficult to learn. Try to look at it from the children's point of view. It only seems easy to you because you've been buttoning and zipping for years.

The 2- and 3-year-olds can learn the simpler parts of dressing. They may manage to pull on a hat, but gloves or even mittens will be difficult. Children of this age may be more able to get clothes off than back on again. For example, they may be able to pull pants or loose trousers down to go to the toilet, but they often get the clothes twisted as they heave them back up again

Children over 5 are mostly capable of dressing and undressing themselves. Some children will still have trouble with fastenings, especially if they panic because someone is telling them to hurry. Shoelaces are especially difficult, as is the kind of coat zip that opens at the end.

Play and clothes

Ideally children should be wearing clothes in which they can play and move about easily. Your preferences for clothes may not be the parents' choice and you should approach any conversation about clothes with consideration for parents' views. For example, some Muslim families will not be happy for their daughters to strip off for dance. You will need to find some compromise between easy movement and modesty.

Take care

Part of the first contact with parents will be describing your programme of play and explaining that children won't be able to enjoy their play *and* keep their clothes perfect.

Make sure that you protect children's clothes with overalls and aprons in activities. When children do get paint or glue on their clothes, pass on any tips to parents – some paint needs to be rinsed out in cold water before normal washing.

Afro-Caribbean girls may have their hair in intricate plaits and possibly oiled as well. Parents will be cross if they find sand or earth in their daughter's hair. It's impossible to get out without abandoning the whole style. Talk with parents about a scarf or other head covering that their child will be willing to wear when she's playing with sand.

Feeding themselves

Children of 2–3 years are more confident and slightly neater in eating and drinking. It's wise to have a meal table that can be wiped up easily, since there will be many spills and drips.

Some foods will be harder than others for children to cut up and get into their mouths. You can encourage children by letting them have a go when it's realistic for them to try, and then by helping them.

Most 5-year-olds are able to feed themselves by whatever method of eating they have learned. This may be chopsticks, fingers, knives and forks, spoons or using bread or a similar food as a utensil. Remember that even older children may still need help sometimes, and they will occasionally lose control of a utensil and inadvertently shoot food off a plate.

ACTIVITY

Children appreciate a chance to practise the common fastenings when there is no pressure of time. Make a material book or cardboard display that gives:

- a button and buttonhole;
- poppers;
- shoelaces;
- a zip.

ACTIVITY

Write down what you could say tactfully to the parents in the following example:

> You are concerned because a 6 year old girl is wearing slip-on shoes and they fall off as she runs. She fell heavily today in the playground.

Talk with your supervisor about your ideas.

Personal care

You can continue to teach children good habits such as washing their hands after going to the toilet and before eating or helping with food. Care of teeth and skin care is covered in section 6.5.

Hair care

Children learn to brush or comb their hair if it is loose, although they will hurt themselves if they tug at tangles. You will need a different kind of comb if children have a head of thick, curly hair – very likely if they are of Afro-Caribbean origin.

Special concerns may arise over hair care and head coverings, and you should make notes in each child's record. For example:

- Boys from Rastafarian families may have their hair in dreadlocks – which should not be combed.
- Young Sikh boys have a small cloth covering over their hair which is wound up neatly on the top of their head. You shouldn't remove this covering.
- Strict Muslim families require that their daughters keep their heads covered with an appropriate large scarf. Girls from Rastafarian families may also be expected to keep their hair covered.

If you are in any doubt, talk with parents. It is far better to admit that you are unsure, rather than to risk upsetting either children or parents by making a wrong move out of ignorance.

Toilet training

Individual differences

Children vary in the age at which they are ready to cooperate in toilet training and how long, overall, it takes. The usual pattern with children does include some steps back as well as progress forwards.

Toilet training is a development that is particularly likely to be affected if a child is upset or worried. The arrival of a new baby or some other change that looms large in a child's world may disrupt training or lead the child to be uncooperative for a while.

Why should children bother?

If you think for a short while, you will realise that getting toilet trained is something that a child does initially to please the adults in her life. So your encouragement is very important through the weeks and months of toilet training a child.

A baby or toddler who tries to feed herself has the immediate pleasure of getting the food in as well as any encouraging reaction from an adult. A child who is lucky enough to pass urine or a bowel movement while sitting on the pot or the toilet has only the adult's pleasure to keep her going. There was no problem before – nappies and adults to change them are a marvellous invention. Eventually children will feel more comfortable in dry pants and will want you to change them if they wet themselves.

When are they ready?

There is little point in starting to toilet train children until they are aware of when they are urinating or passing a bowel movement.

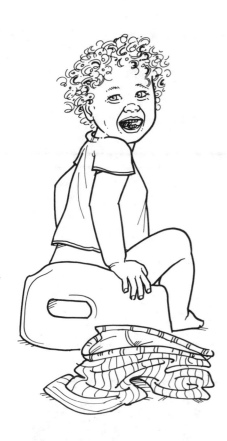

You will see a different expression on their face. Some children of 18–24 months show by clutching themselves or crossing their legs that they are just about to need the toilet.

How to toilet train

The basic steps in toilet training are as follows:

- When a child seems ready to try, you encourage her to sit for a short while on the pot or toilet several times a day. If a child prefers the toilet, you will need a special seat that rests within the existing toilet seat – otherwise children will feel unsafe.

- If she urinates or passes a bowel movement while she is sitting on the pot or toilet, you say something like 'Well done'.

- When she has only a few wet or soiled nappies within the day, you suggest that she could try pants. You need to encourage regular visits to the pot or toilet since she is unlikely to remember without help.

- There will be toileting accidents. Be patient with her; she's not being dirty. Be pleased with her every time she uses the pot or toilet successfully and continue to be encouraging for some months.

Many 3-year-olds are toilet trained for the daytime but you should still expect occasional wet pants. Children cannot hold on very long once they realise they need to go to the toilet. They may also wet themselves if they have a long nap.

Older children, certainly those of primary school age, may want privacy in the toilet. If centre policy is not to have bolts on the door – for safety – then workers should do their best to ensure that other children don't barge in.

Special problems

Children with physical disabilities may have more difficulty in achieving control, or it may never be within their grasp. Much will depend on the nature of their disability. Those 4- and 5-year-olds who are incontinent will start to feel embarrassed and will need your discreet and kind help.

Most children over 5 years have full control of their bladders and bowels by day and night. Families with children who are still having problems should seek help. If parents ask for your advice, then suggest that they start with their doctor or the local clinic.

Caring and helping children to learn

You have important responsibilities in caring well for children from 2 to 8 years old, and in sharing the care effectively with the children's parents. You need to remember that at the same time as you care for children's diet or help them to become toilet trained you are building a relationship with them. You will enable children to add to their abilities and to practise what they know, including their language skills. You will find opportunities to help children's development through the care routines as well as during play activities.

8 Playing with babies and children

This chapter deals with:

● how children learn through play;
● how to offer a broad range of play activities.

8.1 Learning through play

Children from all cultures and at all times in history have played. The games have varied but all children want to experiment with their skills and enjoy different materials and equipment.

Helping children to learn through play

You can help babies and young children learn through play activities. Part of your responsibility will be organising and laying out activities, but it's also important that you often join the children in what they are doing.

Some toys will be bought

If you don't have some piece of equipment, you can improvise

Enjoy yourself

When you join in or lead an activity you should be enthusiastic about what you're doing. Children will lose interest if you sound as if you don't really care what happens next in a story or if you keep losing track in a card game.

Join in

If you sit down with the children you will be closer to their eye level and they will be more able to ask easily for help. You can show them how to handle material such as play dough or ways to build with the bricks. Young children are more likely to concentrate when an adult stays sitting with them.

If you're playing chasing or hiding games, then children will much prefer that you run around as enthusiastically as they do. You can explain if there is a reason for you to sit out of the game – perhaps you have a tired child on your lap.

TO THINK ABOUT

Consider the range of play activities that you offer to the children. Write down *two* activities that you usually watch from the sidelines and two that you join. Discuss with your supervisor your reasons for watching rather than joining in.

You will also be able to keep children safer by joining in

Old favourites and new activities

You need to offer a mix of familiar activities and some new ideas. Both you and the children will be bored if it's always the same kind of painting or never any new songs. However children also learn by repeating a similar activity to gain practice. For example, you will see how a 3-year-old enjoys the ease with which he can now complete a particular jigsaw.

Don't take over their play

You can help children learn through play but only if you respect the boundaries that the children have determined, and don't appear to take the game over. For example, if you're asked to be a patient in their imaginary hospital, you should play your part with equal seriousness as the children. You can still introduce new ideas to the game – perhaps gently challenge one child's claim that men can't be nurses.

Encouraging varied play

If you are closely involved with children's play you'll be more able to encourage children to try a new activity or to approach a familiar game in a novel way. You will be more likely to succeed in encouraging a child to join a group of which you are already a part. Perhaps you are concerned that a child has difficulty sharing equipment with other children and you need to be beside her to avoid any arguments.

Workers who are involved in play can also encourage children away from rigid attitudes about different play for the sexes. For example, John can show that he knows what he's doing at the sewing table and Marissa shows she can play football.

Learning from different activities

Most activities will allow children to learn in more than one area of development. For example, a group of children who are enjoying the contents of the dressing up box will be making choices and sharing out the items, practising the fastenings on clothes and exercising their communication skills.

You would be right to be concerned if a child was very hard to interest in any activity but don't worry if she isn't keen on just one or two. For instance, one 3-year-old may not like threading large beads. She can practise fine physical skills just as successfully through painting, building with small constructional materials and cutting up her food.

> **ACTIVITY**
>
> List three activities in the centre that could help 4- and 5-year-olds to learn the coordination they will need for writing.

Broadening children's awareness

You need to select materials, games, songs and books to reflect the cultural traditions of children who are within the group. You also have the responsibility to widen children's understanding of the world beyond their own neighbourhood.

Talking about activities

As you get to know children as individuals you can help them to make links between what they have managed before and what they are attempting now. Once children have learned to talk, you can also provide continuity through your conversation – reminding them through words as well as showing by actions.

You need to be sensitive to how much you add, in words or actions, to a child's play. Children get irritated if they can't do anything without a worker commenting or questioning them. A common mistake is to leave children no space to reply, perhaps by trying to move on too quickly to another child or group. Don't forget about listening and looking, as well as the talking. Look back at Chapter 3.

Sharing and taking turns

You can teach children the value of sharing out limited resources if you realise that waiting and taking turns are not easy. A short time to you will seem ages to a 3-year-old. It's your responsibility to make sure that children who wait for their turn aren't elbowed out of the way by less patient peers. You need to help children to see how both they and others will benefit if nobody grabs all the bricks. Showing works much better than simply telling them they 'must share'.

> **ACTIVITY**
>
> Watch a group of children playing at the sand tray.
> List two abstract concepts that they could be learning through this experience. You can look back at section 5.4 to remind you about abstract concepts.

> **ACTIVITY**
>
> Look at the image of the world that is given by the books, toys and wall illustrations in your centre.
> For instance, could you see yourself portrayed positively or at all, if you were:
>
> - a father who enjoyed playing with his children;
> - an Asian mother;
> - a girl who liked playing football;
> - a child with a disability that required a wheelchair;
> - a child who lived on a farm.
>
> Discuss your observations with your supervisor. What changes could be made in the play materials if they ignore any of the above?

Should you ever stop a game?

Occasionally the content of children's play will concern you and you may decide to step in after discussing your worries with your supervisor. You would need a different approach for different situations as the following examples show:

- 3 year old Nadine is small for her age. You have noticed on three occasions that she is told by other children that she *has* to be the baby as they play families in the home corner.

You should watch to see whether Nadine manages to refuse the role of baby and still be allowed to play. If it looks as if she needs your help you could intervene saying something like, 'Nadine has been the baby three times lately. I think she deserves a go as Mummy or Daddy now'. You may be able to help further by joining the children's play.

- A group of five boys are regularly playing a loud and aggressive-looking game based on a popular television series.

If the boys are knocking over other children in their game then you would have good reason to say, 'That's enough now, you're hurting the others'. Watch the group of boys and see whether they are playing other games as well. If their spontaneous play has become restricted to this one game, you will need to intervene. It won't be helpful just to tell the boys to stop, you'll have to offer an alternative that allows them still to run about and call out.

- You find two 4-year-olds playing families in the home corner. They have removed each other's pants.

This situation is not unusual because children are often interested in each other's bodies – especially the bits that are usually covered up. Your best approach is to suggest that they get dressed and say calmly that, 'Everybody keeps their pants on in the centre unless they need to go to the toilet'. You shouldn't tell the children they have been naughty or dirty because they haven't. You should be concerned if either a child persists in wanting to play this game rather than other kinds of play or is showing a level of sexual awareness that seems unusual to you. Talk with your supervisor about your concerns. Section 4.3 covers children at risk from abuse.

Planning ahead

You should plan ahead for at least a week so that you can be sure that you are offering a varied programme of activities to children. You can build some of the activities around a theme for the week, such as 'homes' or 'shapes'.

You'll need to plan in cooperation with other workers, especially those in the same room as you. Give the children a choice between activities when possible – although this may not be realistic if you're working in a very small room.

You should prepare activities so that children do not have to wait too long. Sometimes part of the activity will be that children help you lay out toys or hand round the drinks. You can explain to children what you have planned and this information will help them to feel part of the day, even if they are too young to remember all the details.

ACTIVITY

Suppose that you were watching a group doing pretend cooking. Two of the girls tell a boy to go away with 'Boys don't cook'.

Note down what you could say and what you might do to deal with this situation. Discuss your ideas with your supervisor.

ACTIVITY

Plan a week's programme for your group. Write down what you will do each day and make a note of preparations you need to make in advance or if you need to consult anyone else. Your plan might start like this:

Date: Monday 5th February

Time	*Activity*	*Reminders*
9.00	Cutting and sticking with coloured paper shapes	Cut shapes out as soon as I arrive
	Water tray with blue water	Find blue colouring
	Dressing up clothes out	
10.00	Drink time	Billy's turn to help
10.30	Play in the garden – bikes, hoops, skipping ropes	Show how to skip Chalk shapes on paving
11.30	Story time	'The hungry caterpillar', Gaven's request from Friday
12.15	Lunch	Sajida's turn to help me dish up
1.15	Sleep and quiet time	Make play dough for tomorrow
	Jigsaws	
	Play picture lotto when I've made the dough	
2.15	Trip to library	Can Marie still have some of my group?

And so on...

Children can enjoy outdoor play even when the weather isn't perfect

Reviewing a programme

At the end of each week, think about the activities you did with the children. You can look at the programme from your point of view:

- Which activities did the children seem to enjoy the most?
- Which activities didn't hold their attention as well as you had hoped? What do you think were the reasons?

- Make a note of what you have learned that will help your future plans. It's also a good idea to find out what the children think and to note it down. You can ask them:
- 'What do you think was the best thing we did this week?' or
- 'What would you most like to do next week?'

Children of 3 and 4 years will often express an opinion if you invite them, and they will be pleased that you asked.

8.2 A varied play programme

Physical games

All children need exercise for healthy development. They need to practise the physical skills they have already achieved and acquire new skills in a safe environment.

Games with babies and toddlers

The best games for babies are physical play with you. Most babies like to be stroked, cuddled and tickled gently. They will often laugh if you make funny noises or faces. Some babies relish being lifted up and some enjoy quite vigorous movements. You'll discover what an individual baby likes.

Babies of 6 months and older like to play endless peek-a-boo when they or you keep disappearing behind a cloth or a large magazine. They often initiate a game of making faces and noises with you or in a mirror. Some babies will show with smiles that they recognise a game of movements to a song.

Babies and toddlers also like toys to bash and rattle about. They like games in which they throw or drop a toy and you keep returning it. Children under 2 years can be interested in anything that catches their attention – because it's bright or makes an interesting sound. Children under 2 years are also fascinated by putting small objects into and out of larger containers.

Mobile toddlers like to be chased and play hide and seek – you obviously have to slow down if you are not to catch them too easily. They are delighted if you get down on your hands and knees and crawl as well. Even children who can walk and run with ease enjoy this game of crawling chasing – although it can be hard on your knees, even if the floor covering is soft.

Games with young children

As young children gain in physical confidence, they will benefit from all of the following kinds of physical play:

- Running about, climbing and jumping in a safe play environment and on secure equipment.

- A choice of play vehicles suitable for the age group. The 2-year-olds are able to use push along bikes, and 3- and 4-year-olds need tricycles. Children like to use wheeled carts in which they can load up toys and other objects and transport them around.

- A choice of outdoor equipment such as bats and balls of different sizes, hoops and skipping ropes.

Children find new ways to use their skills

ACTIVITY

Start a list in your work file on physical games to play with children. Make a note of the name of a game and how it is played. You might include, for example:

Hide and seek – in an enclosed space, such as the centre garden, one seeker counts up to 20 while the others hide. You should help the child seeker and at 20 you call out 'Coming ready or not!' The 3- and 4-year-olds will not be well hidden so you should pretend that they are hard to find, saying things such as, 'I wonder where Jamie can be?'
Snails' race – the children have a 'race' along a short distance, but the aim is to move as slowly as possible and not to be the first.

ACTIVITY

Give a group of 3- or 4-year-olds several large cardboard boxes, along with some material and clothes such as hats. Watch what they do – left to the resources of their own imagination. Note down the games that they develop and how you could use this information in your future plans. For example, do they try to make a tent out of the materials but really need some help from you?

Joining in the games

Children will enjoy a lot of physical play with each other, although they will like you to admire their skill in how fast they can run or how well they can jump. Children will need you to organise games with simple rules – see the activity. You can also introduce new ways of playing with the existing equipment. You could lay out an obstacle course using different equipment for climbing over and crawling through, or mark out a track for children to steer round on the bikes.

Play equipment such as bats and balls will help children to practise the fine coordinations of throwing, catching or hitting, but they will need your help. You will be able to show children how to hold a bat and you will have more patience than another child in throwing a ball gently so that a 4-year-old has a chance of catching it.

Play to stretch the imagination

Between 18 and 24 months, children show that they are imagining events and feelings. They start to put dolls or teddies to bed, pretend to feed them or tell them off. Children's imaginative play will grow with a choice of play materials and the encouragement to use them. For example:

- Some 2-year-olds may start to have simple pretend tea parties involving dolls or other children. Children of 3–4 years sometimes organise elaborate pretend meals, to which you may also be invited. Children will bring their own family's ways in child care or cooking to their pretend play. You should not direct children in a way that implies that what they are doing is wrong. For example, the English way of brewing tea is first to boil the water in a kettle but in many countries around the world people boil water in a small saucepan.

- A well-equipped home corner can provide the children with an opportunity to play out long sequences of events in which they each play a role. With only slight changes, the same corner can become a hospital, a school, a hairdressers' salon or a shop.

- Children of 3–4 years will enjoy taking part in short plays and by 5 or 6 years will be ready for simple drama or mime.

Children's pretend play will include what they have observed. You may be surprised by how accurately some children copy adults' words and actions. You may see and hear your own way of behaving in how children play with a doll or organise a pretend meal.

Natural materials

Children like to explore natural materials through feel and smell as well as sight. You have to watch young children very carefully since they don't distinguish the hygienic materials from the unsafe. You could offer all of the following activities at different times.

Sand and water

These materials can be used indoors in purpose-built trays on wheels. Otherwise a large plastic bowl will provide the space to fill and empty containers, or to pour material from one container to another. You can vary the activity by the toys that you add to the sand or water. Sand can be wet or dry, and water play can be varied by adding different colours or introducing a mixture to make bubbles.

Play dough

Dough is a very flexible material. It's ideal for pretend cooking as well as making shapes and any kind of modelling. Children can work with their hands and fingers as well as learn to use rollers and plastic cutters. You can discourage younger children from trying to eat the dough – adding salt to the mixture gives it an unpleasant taste, as well as making it last longer.

Using the outdoors

An outdoor sand pit can give children more elbow room. If you can put up a paddling pool you must supervise children very closely. A sunny day may be the perfect opportunity to let the children scrub up some of the toys in the water tray. You will be less concerned outside by splashes and overflows.

Making collections

You can use trips out with children to observe and collect natural materials. Even quite small open spaces can be a source of flowers, leaves, twigs and different kinds of nuts – not all edible, of course. Young children often like selecting stones which you could later wash and display. You should thoroughly wash any such material as birds' feathers.

You can help children to organise their collections and lay them out on a table or make a wall display. You should write a short explanation of the display – for example, 'We found some coloured stones in the park'.

Domestic play

Children can be happily occupied for long periods with pretend meals, shopping and organising a home corner. They also need the opportunity to join in real activities such as gardening, cooking, tidying up and cleaning. Some ideas follow, but look also at section 7.3.

Growing things

If you have access to a garden you may be able to plant flower seeds or edible plants such as tomatoes. Indoor growing can work just as well and can be arranged so that children can more easily see what the plants are doing.

For example, children can plant seeds in small pots or egg boxes. You should pick the faster growing varieties of flowers, vegetables or herbs. You can also grow cress on damp paper towels or bean sprouts in jam jars. Another method is to grow green shoots from the cut-off tops of carrots or turnips in a saucer of water.

Cooking

Even if you can't take children into the kitchen, you can allow children to arrange food. For instance, 3- and 4-year-olds enjoy laying out crackers and cakes to make a pattern. If you cut up a selection of fruit and raw vegetables, such as carrots, they will like making an attractive display and then eating it for a snack.

When you arrange a cooking activity you should let children join in fully with the pouring, weighing and stirring. You can simplify cooking for children as young as 2 or 3 years. You can for example:

- prepare a gingerbread biscuit mix and then let the children roll and cut the shapes;
- make the most of letting them decorate the finished product, for instance, making faces on biscuits with currants;
- use mixes such as bread dough which are more tolerant of handling than pastry – rolls made by children are often more edible than jam tarts because pastry becomes tough if it is handled too much.

Creative activities

Children like to make things, and they have a sense of pride when these are displayed. The choice of arts and crafts is so wide that you will find something to engage the attention of children from 18 months or so upwards. Your task is to simplify the activity so that younger children can do as much as possible themselves. By all means help children if they ask, but don't take over. The point is to have an array of works that the children have done themselves.

Painting and drawing

The 2- and 3-year-olds need fat crayons and thick brushes. They won't manage the grip needed for fine pencils and they will press so hard that they will splay out a thin brush. Many 4-year-olds are becoming more able to use

---

ACTIVITY

Start a list in your work file of recipes suitable for cooking activities with children – for example, mixes that can be stirred rather than needing lengthy beating and recipes that need little or no heat.

Some tasty concoctions can be made by combining crushed biscuits or cereals such as corn-flakes with melted chocolate or syrup.

finer brushes or crayons. By 5–7 years children will definitely need thin as well as thick paint brushes, and crayons and pencils with a point – not too sharp.

If you lay out a choice of colours in paints or crayons, then children can use different colours for their own effects in free style painting and drawing. Make sure that you have a range of different skin tones in paints for faces and bodies. You can admire the use of shapes or colours in a child's painting but don't press them to tell you what is depicted. They'll soon tell you if it's 'Mummy' or 'a train'.

You can introduce stencil shapes and printed sheets for colouring in patterns. Children may be able to cut some shapes themselves but you can help by sometimes preparing cutouts of animals, flowers or kinds of transport when you are following a theme in play activities.

There are many different ways for children to paint and draw, and you can make changes to an activity to allow for children's abilities. Some examples are:

- Children can use chalks as a change – on boards or on card for a different effect. Don't be surprised if the younger ones cannot help but snap the longer pieces of chalk.
- You can show them how to paint on one side of a sheet of paper and then to fold it to give a butterfly effect.
- Help children to make marbled paper by laying it gently on the surface of an oil-on-water mix with colours added.
- Vary the thickness of paint or mix it with substances such as sugar so that children can produce different textures.
- Show them how to print with shapes cut from chunks of vegetables or using leaves covered with thick paint.
- Organise hand and foot printing. This takes two workers – one to help children make the print and one to wash their hand or foot straight afterwards.

Creative writing

Some 3-year-olds and many 4-year-olds have learned to press less hard with a crayon or pencil. They are ready to start the finer work that will give them important practice in the skills they will need for writing.

Children are learning careful coordination between what they see and what they draw. They can practise by any of the following methods:

- making or copying shapes and patterns;
- joining the dots in prepared sheets;
- learning how to trace;
- marking the way through a simple maze on paper.

Children of 3 and 4 years can help to make books. They do the illustrations and dictate the story for you to write down – or to type if your centre has a computer. Place the sheets between two pieces of card and thread the spine through two or more holes that you make through card and paper. If you staple the sheets you must tape over the metal.

By 5–6 years children can enjoy trying to write down some of the story. Don't correct their spelling until they are more confident in getting ideas onto paper. Then you can help children to spell a few words each time.

Children develop a preference for their right or left hand and you must respect their choice. You may need to show some 4- and 5-year-olds how to hold a pencil with fingers and thumb rather than a whole hand grip.

ACTIVITY

Find out the range of art and craft materials in your centre. Talk with your supervisor about the activities offered to the children and add any ideas to your file.

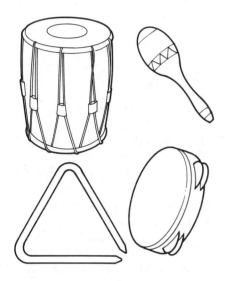

You will find information and songs in Jean Gilbert, *Festivals*, Oxford University Press, 1986.

Needlework

Conventional sewing is difficult for children under 5 years and can be dangerous because of the sharp needles. You can offer a safer and easier version by using large hole tapestry, called binca, and blunt needles with large eye holes. You should sit with children who are sewing – they will need a lot of help and could still hurt themselves if they're careless.

If you cut out shapes from binca – perhaps 15 cm by 15 cm – 4- and 5-year-olds can make patterns and produce a small mat. Using the same blunt-ended needles, children can also sew with thread or wool onto polystyrene trays or picture sewing cards.

Music

There are several different ways in which you can use music in your activities. If you are able to play a musical instrument you will be able to use this skill, but it's not essential.

● Singing

Babies around the world like people to sing to them. They like lively songs with gestures and plenty of expression. Sometimes they like the soft, quiet songs and these may soothe them if they are upset.

Toddlers often start to join in familiar songs and rhymes. Even if they can't say the words, they copy the rhythm of what you are singing. Often 3- and 4-year-olds will sing the words and may like to sing in front of the group. You can encourage children to have a go but don't press them.

Children under 8 years will enjoy your singing to them and with them. They are unlikely to criticise the quality of your voice, so there is no need to feel self-conscious.

The source of some of your songs may be religious festivals which you celebrate in your centre – for example Christmas or Chinese New Year. Talk with your supervisor about how to explain festivals simply yet with respect.

● Listening to and playing music

You can draw from different cultures for your songs and rhymes and for music tapes or CDs that you play to children. You will also give them more scope in making their own instruments if you take ideas from several musical traditions.

● Dancing

Toddlers like moving to music and some 3- and 4-year-olds can be inventive dancers with their own steps and dance style. Children will enjoy expressing themselves through simple dance sequences and pretending to be animals or trees blown in the wind. You can play music that varies in mood and volume.

Building and modelling

Children develop their ability to coordinate eye and hand. They use this ability in activities such as painting and physical skills like bike riding or learning to dress themselves. Constructional materials provide another source of experience.

Collage and junk modelling

When you and the children make a collage or a model, they are able to use and practise a number of different skills. Suppose that you are all making a large caterpillar out of circles. They could practise cutting out circles that you had drawn. They could paint or decorate the circles in their own way from the materials you put out. Then they would work with you to place and stick the circles before you fix the whole caterpillar on the wall and label it with 'We made a caterpillar with circles'.

The best materials for collage are often free or very cheap. Washed and flattened milk bottle tops are very effective as patterns or for children to arrange and stick to make a tall building on paper or a spaceship. Children can handle different shapes and colours of pasta, scraps of material and wool.

Junk modelling uses safe materials that otherwise go in the waste bin – egg boxes, cardboard tubes, polystyrene shapes, supermarket food trays or yogurt pots. Wash and dry any container that has held food or drink.

Even toddlers can make a satisfying collage or a model, and you can offer help with their project. Children of 4 and 5 years can make substantial creations out of junk material.

Building

Children under 2 years enjoy building up piles or wobbly towers. They get as much fun from knocking over what they have made as from building it in the first place.

Before they are able to build like the 3- and 4-year-olds, toddlers have to become aware of relative size and shape – of what will fit together. Posting boxes can be a good way of exploring, especially if shapes make a satisfying clunk when they are successfully posted through the correct space.

Children need plenty of basic building items such as wooden blocks and plastic bricks and shapes that will fix together. You need larger sizes for 2- and 3-year-olds who will be frustrated by small items that they can't manipulate. They may also put little shapes in their mouths

Jigsaws

Completing a jigsaw requires children to apply more than one skill. They have to be able to pick up pieces and manipulate them into a space. However, children also need to learn an experimental approach – this piece won't fit in this way up, so maybe it will if I turned it around.

It's possible to get very simple jigsaws that will interest toddlers yet not be too difficult. Very young children are helped by those jigsaws that have knobs for holding the pieces.

Completing jigsaws is more challenging than you might think and children often need your assistance. You can help without taking over the activity. You can ease the frustration of an ambitious 2-year-old by partly completing a jigsaw that has fascinated him. The 3- and 4-year-olds often need such advice as 'Turn it round and try again'.

As children tackle jigsaws with more pieces, you can show them strategies such as looking for the corner bits and the pieces with straight edges. Some 6- and 7-year-olds will be ready for a big jigsaw which you all do together over several days.

Board games

Some 3- and 4-year-olds are ready for very simple board or card games. Children need to be able to sit down for as long as 10 minutes and be willing to follow basic rules in a game. Use your judgement as to whether you should simplify rules even further. The 5- and 6-year-olds will be able to learn card games like 'Happy Families' in which children are collecting sets.

First of all you should try out the picture versions of games such as snap, dominoes or lotto. Since children have to match identical pictures they get practice in looking carefully as well as waiting for their turn.

So long as you don't have too large a group, you may be able to help 4- and 5-year-olds to play board games needing dice. The big dice which are a

ACTIVITY

During the next two weeks put out the different constructional sets available in your centre. Watch and note which materials seem to interest the children most. In your opinion which sets seem to provide the most possibilities for layouts and buildings? You can ask children which sets they like the best.

Discuss your observation and opinions with your supervisor.

2–3 cm cube are easier for children to handle and to see the dots. You will need to help them to count the dots and the squares round the board. The best games will be those where the consequence of landing on a particular square is obvious from the illustration – for example, snakes and ladders.

You will have to be patient as children learn, since they will get confused sometimes. You will have to ensure that older children are patient with the younger ones.

Books and stories

Children under 3 years old

Babies and toddlers can start to enjoy books. You will need a selection of books that will survive rough treatment while you are showing the children how to treat books with care. Any centre which is attended by children under 3 years should have strong cardboard or material books as well as books with paper pages.

Babies and very young children enjoy looking at books composed of pictures and photographs but only short sentences of text. You can chat about the pictures or make up a simple story line. Be ready to repeat your story many times.

Children under 2 or 3 years are easily distracted unless they have your individual attention. So you will find young children start to fidget if they are part of a group to whom you are reading or telling a story. Try to look at books sometimes with only two or three very young children.

Children's attention is always best held if they are involved in an activity rather than sitting passively, and you especially need to involve young children as individuals. Choose books with a story line that relates closely to the illustrations. Children's interest will also be held when they get to know a story or they can join in a short phrase that is repeated through the book.

ACTIVITY

When you give children the choice, which books or songs do they ask for again and again? Note these down. In your opinion why do the children especially enjoy these books or songs? Discuss your observation with your supervisor and use your ideas to choose new material.

You will have to work to hold their attention

Reading

Children will enjoy your reading out loud to them as well as your company as you look at books and chat together. Reading out loud to a group of children is a skilled activity that you will need to practise. The following suggestions will help:

● A group of children becomes fidgety quite quickly. It's better to have two or three short stories that hold their attention than a longer one which loses the attention of half of the group.

- Let children choose some of the books that you read – be ready to have old favourites as well as new books.

- Be sure that you know a story well enough that you can turn the book towards the children for them to see the illustrations. You need to look at the children at least as much as you look at the pages of the book.

- Speak more slowly than normal conversation speed and take pauses, especially as you turn a page, and it makes sense to say something like, 'And what happened next was...'.

- Vary the sound of your voice by sometimes speaking more quietly or slowly. Change how you speak according to the story line, for example, if a character in the book is cross then let your voice show that feeling.

- Smile at the children during story time and sound as if you are wondering what will happen next even if you have read this book many times.

Children over 5 years

Don't stop reading out loud to children just because they are learning to read for themselves. The 5-, 6- and 7-year-olds need you to listen as they practise their reading skills, but they still like you to read them stories.

Some groups of 4-year-olds and definitely 5- and 6-year-olds enjoy a longer book which you read in episodes spread over several days. At the beginning of each reading you should recall the main events of the story so far – not everything – and the point where you stopped last time. Don't do the recap all by yourself – ask the children, 'Who can remember where we finished in the story yesterday?'

Story telling

Sometimes you can tell a story rather than read out loud. You might tell the story from one of the books, but you illustrate it with pictures that you stick up on a board as the tale unfolds.

Some people have a talent for creating original tales – use this skill if you are able. You could also talk to parents and see if any of them are good story tellers, especially if they can recount folk tales from different cultures.

Trips out and about

Permission and safety

You should always check that you have parents' permission for the kind of trip that you are planning. Talk with your supervisor about how many adults you need for the number of children involved. Your centre should have a clear policy determined by local authority guidelines.

Any trips involving transport should be carefully checked to ensure that the commercial companies have accident and liability insurance. You will need to tell your insurance company if you will be transporting children in your own car as part of your work. Any car or coach must have child seat belts or other restraints appropriate to the age of the children.

Local trips

Babies and children enjoy a change of scene. Trips out don't have to be lengthy or expensive:

- Children enjoy visiting a post office or bank so long as the queue isn't too long and you let them choose a couple of forms to take away.

ACTIVITY

Watch an experienced worker as he or she reads a story to a group of children. How does he involve children in the activity? How does she deal with children who aren't listening? Talk with the worker afterwards and ask for tips. Note down the practical suggestions in your file.

ACTIVITY

Some books offer a way to approach sad or upsetting events, such as going into hospital or divorce. Talk with the librarian in the local children's library and note what is available. Talk with your supervisor about how you should introduce such books to children and under what circumstances you should discuss your plans with parents.

- Trips to the local shops or the market are especially interesting if you buy something for later – perhaps some fruit or rolls.
- Even a small park may have a range of flowers or shrubs and a small pond may have baby ducks in springtime.

Young children are safe in a buggy and they can see well

ACTIVITY

In your work file start a list of local trips which are either free or very cheap. Note down the trips that you have done with the children and ask other workers for their ideas.

Some trips continue to give enjoyment as you reminisce about them later. Children enjoy talking about what went wrong just as much, if not more, than the sights that you had wanted to show them. A trip to the nearby market may be remembered for weeks because your hat blew off and was squashed by a bus.

Sometimes it's worth extending a trip by a follow-up activity. For example, on a trip to the park the children might collect leaves and twigs. On the next day you could all use the collection in a painting or sticking activity.

Day outings

From time to time you may be able to arrange trips further afield. These will require careful organisation and you will need up-to-date information on the place you wish to visit.

You could find out about a leisure complex or a historic building by sending off for a leaflet and making a telephone enquiry. It's worth discussing a proposed trip with any adults – workers or parents – who know the venue. For example, they may be able to warn you that the wheelchair access to the toy museum is difficult or that the beach you planned to visit has become polluted.

ACTIVITY

In your work file design a countdown checklist for day trips with the children. Start the list like this:

- Venue for the trip – Where? Do we have up to date information? What will it cost?
- Transport – How will we get there? Cost? Safety concerns such as insurance, seat belts?
- Supervision – How many adults will we need? Do we need the help of parents?

Discuss with your supervisor how you will need to expand this list to cover timings of a trip and what you will need to take with you, for instance, food or changes of clothes for children.

---

9 Getting along – your behaviour, children's behaviour

This chapter deals with the practical issues of:

- how children learn to behave;
- appropriate ways of handling children's behaviour.

9.1 How do children learn to behave

Children are not born to be good or bad in their behaviour; they learn ways of behaving. They copy the behaviour of other children and adults' behaviour as well. Children also react to how they are treated by the adults in their life. So you can influence how children learn to behave.

It's not unusual for children to behave better for some people than for others. Perhaps they have learned that they can't get away with things with one person, or one person is more encouraging to the children and so they want to please him or her.

If you want to help children to behave well, remember that they need:

- to understand what you want from them;
- to be motivated to cooperate and make the effort;
- you to set a good example for them to follow.

The practical suggestions in this chapter will help you on each of these points.

Realistic expectations

Even the most cooperative of children won't be well behaved all the time. If you insist on perfect behaviour all the time, some children will stop trying because you're too hard to please. Some children will be distressed because they can never meet your standards.

You also have to allow for children's ages – a realistic expectation for a 5-year-old would be silly to apply to a 2-year-old. Look back at Chapter 5 for descriptions of children's development from birth to 8 years.

Babies

There's no such thing as a 'good' baby. Babies can't be either well behaved or naughty; they simply do what comes naturally to extremely young human-beings. Babies who cry for apparently no reason or fill their nappy just after they've been changed are not setting out to torment you. They aren't capable of planning such a campaign.

At root, of course, you know that. You have to remind yourself when you are tired. You need to see the chance to communicate with babies through

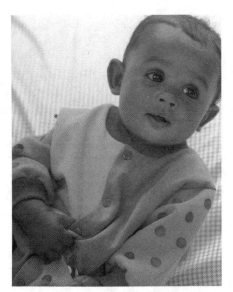

Babies can't be either 'good' or 'naughty'

It's unrealistic to expect children to play neatly – it is realistic to teach them how to tidy up with you

physical care (as described in Chapter 6) or else you can feel worn down by events that seem to be making you work even harder.

Young children are inquisitive

Babies and toddlers will grab anything of interest. They aren't being naughty when they rip a book or pull hard on your hair. They are exploring and finding out; they don't know enough to realise the consequences of what they do.

You need to be ready to:

- say 'no' kindly and firmly;
- distract them into play that won't hurt or be dangerous;
- move them away from a tempting area – words alone are often not enough.

EXAMPLE

Joanne is 2 years old and has learned that she is not allowed to touch the television controls. Her childminder has patiently repeated this each time Joanne has attempted to fiddle and has moved her out of reach.

Now Joanne stretches out to touch and tells herself, 'No'. Her childminder praises her with, 'Well done, Joanne' and offers her a toy to occupy her hands.

Children learn what you want

Children of 2–3 years will start to remember what you want but they will often not understand why you want it. You can explain basic rules very simply. However, do realise that a 2½-year-old may listen to every single word of 'Don't hit Gerry – it hurts him', yet not really grasp your meaning. Young children still struggle with the idea that other people hurt physically and emotionally just like them.

Even 3- and 4-year-olds may understand what you're saying about taking turns on the bike so everyone can have a go. But they might not agree that they should be third in line and they might not want to wait. Young children will learn what you want and they will cooperate more and more if you make it easier for them to do so by your own behaviour.

Children come to appreciate a quiet atmosphere

Children over 4 years understand more about how rules work and can see the point of them. They are more capable of waiting and of seeing another point of view. They will listen more to reason and explanation if they have experienced this kind of behaviour from adults. You will work sometimes with children who have become used to adults who shout but don't follow up or who are inconsistent. Be patient – you will have to show these children your ways.

9.2 Setting limits

ACTIVITY

With the help of your supervisor or an experienced worker make a list of the rules that children are expected to follow in your centre.

Discuss what is covered by the rules. If any rule is worded as 'Don't', try to rephrase it as a 'Do'.

If the list is more than 10 basic rules, discuss with your supervisor which rules are the most important and mark them.

Nobody benefits from really long lists of rules. Any rules should make sense to workers and be straightforward to explain to children. The rules should also be realistic for the age and abilities of the children. You should get into the habit of thanking children for doing what you wish. Make sure that you make such encouraging remarks at least as often as you draw children's attention to what you don't want them to do.

Word rules positively

Children find it easier to follow a 'Do' than a 'Don't'. For example:

- It's easier to follow, 'Keep the sand in the sand tray, please' than 'Don't throw it on the floor'.
- A rule of 'One at a time on the slide' is a more practical message than 'No shoving and pushing'.

A few rules will need to be worded as 'Don't' but the reasons must be explained positively. You will find that in many centres children will be told firmly 'Don't use that word' if they swear or use terms that are racially abusive. Children should also be given an explanation that a word is rude or that what they have said to another child is very unkind. What is said will depend of course on the age of the children involved.

ACTIVITY

Take the list of centre rules that you discussed in the previous activity. With a partner take turns to explain simply and briefly the reason for each of the rules. One of you should note down the explanation. Discuss with your supervisor whether the explanations would be simple enough for a 3-, 5- or 7-year-old.

Saying and explaining

It will rarely be enough to tell children once. For instance, you will need to remind some children many times that you want them to hang their coats on the peg and not drop them on the floor.

As hard as it can be sometimes, repeat what you need to say kindly and patiently. Thank children warmly for what they have done – even if they took a bit of persuading.

Children don't respect adults who won't give their reasons. They're unimpressed by, 'Do it because I say so' and at 3 or 4 years they will notice if you break your own rules. You should be ready to explain why you wish the children to behave one way rather than another, but keep your explanations short as well as simple. If children look at you blankly they probably haven't understood what you've said.

You need to realise that adults often use words in a special way or as a kind of shorthand. You may know what you mean if you say, 'Be good' or 'Behave!' to the children, but they may be confused. It's better to be specific – if you want them to stop shouting then say, 'Please be quiet', and support what you say with a gesture like putting your finger to your lips.

The difference between 'telling' and 'telling tales' is one example of how adults sometimes don't explain very well what they mean. For example, you may mean that you want children to come and tell you if they are having troubles with another child; you don't want the first child to start punching the other one. You didn't mean that you want to hear every little gripe, especially when you believe that the children could resolve a disagreement themselves. You would call this behaviour 'telling tales'.

ACTIVITY

Ask an experienced worker which of the centre rules he or she believes the children find more difficult to understand. Note down how the experienced worker shows children how to follow these rules.

Fairness

Children need to know how you expect them to behave and they need to be confident that you will behave fairly towards them. You shouldn't punish one child for doing something that you regularly ignore from another child.

Sometimes you will need to explain to children your reasons for apparently bending your own rules. For example, 3- and 4-year-olds will probably appreciate that a 2-year-old is learning to use utensils, and this is the reason that you are letting the younger child eat with her fingers as well as a spoon. The 3- or 4-year-olds may also understand your approach when you explain, 'I know Nisha called me a rude name. I ignored it because I think she just wants to make me cross'.

When you say 'No', you mean it

It's normal for children to test you out by seeing if you will change your mind if they moan at you or keep on doing something. Children need to learn that you will stand firm on basic rules. Children are reassured by adults who behave as if they are confidently in control. Once you have said, 'Marsha, put the book back now, please', you should watch to make sure that she does put it back. If she doesn't then you will need to act so as to persuade her to do what you have asked. This doesn't have to become a power battle – see section 9.3.

Of course, you need to be sure of the rules you are applying, so that you don't say 'No' without thinking and then regret it.

Consistent boundaries

Children have a right to expect that you are predictable in your time with them. They shouldn't have to wonder whether today is a day that you will let them talk and giggle over lunch or one of your days when you shout at them to be quiet and eat up.

Children also have the right to expect that you follow your own rules:

- If it's no sweets in the nursery, then they shouldn't be able to catch you nibbling on the quiet.

- You will expect them to say 'sorry'. You won't lose children's respect by admitting you sometimes make mistakes. Apologise if you've leapt to a wrong conclusion as swiftly as if you've stepped on someone's toe.

- You will ask the children not to yell and shout. So you must keep shouts for real emergencies. Work to get children's attention before you speak. You could
  – use a loud hand clap if a group is very noisy
  – try lowering your voice sometimes rather than raising it.
     So long as they can see that you are talking, children sometimes quieten to listen since they don't want to miss anything.

Differences between adults

When you're sharing the care of children, it's inevitable adults won't behave in exactly the same way. You should sort out troublesome inconsistencies in private with the adults concerned – don't let the children get caught in the middle.

Disagreements between workers should be resolved within the centre, with the intervention of your supervisor if necessary. You may have to talk and resolve with parents any apparent contradictions between home and centre.

Differences will not always be conflicts. For example:

- 3-year-old Daniel who has just joined the centre may be used at home to having the book of his choice read to him. You have explained to him that in a group you have to take the choices of different children each time but he still looks sad. You take the time to talk with Daniel's father so that he can support your explanation.

ACTIVITY

Ask your supervisor about the most common areas of misunderstanding or conflict between family and centre ways of treating children. Note down these areas and your supervisor's suggestions on what to say to parents.

On other occasions you will be explaining to a parent that you do not allow certain ways of behaving in the centre. For example:

- 4-year-old Stefan wrenches other children off his favourite bike and deals with any argument by hitting. Yesterday, you heard his mother tell Stefan to 'hit him back' when there was a scuffle with another child at going-home time. Someone, if not you, will need to talk to Stefan's mother to explain firmly that nobody – child or adult – is permitted to resolve disputes in the centre by hitting. The worker should explain that hitting between children swiftly gets out of hand. The mother may want to know how you teach children to deal with disagreements.

Some adults react differently to the same kind of behaviour depending on whether the child is a boy or a girl. Perhaps you do this yourself and you may not be aware of it.

9.3 Keeping control and showing warmth

You will motivate children by spending time with them and by being encouraging in your words and actions. You will help children to behave well if you put plenty of energy into showing them that you have noticed. It's sensible that you behave differently when children are doing something they shouldn't – you want them to get a clear message from you. However there are more and less effective ways of dealing with children's misbehaviour.

Ways of encouraging children

Any number of experiences can be encouraging to children. Here are just a few ways:

- Encouraging words that thank a child or recognise her effort. You might say, 'Thank you for picking up the books for me' or 'What a great job you've done washing the paint pots'.
- Many gestures are very encouraging to children – a smile, a cuddle or a friendly touch.
- Children often appreciate a chance to spend some time with you – chatting or doing odd jobs together – and you can offer this as a reward, for example, 'I think I can trust you to take this letter to the office'.
- The chance to help out on a favourite task will often act as an incentive for children to behave well. Centres find that they have to operate a rota for daily tasks such as handing out drinks, since children see this task as special.
- Special treats don't have to be sweets, although they might be occasionally. Treats can be anything that children like and don't get often – a trip to the market for some cherries or getting the special pop-up books out.

When children misbehave

Children are going to misbehave sometimes. When they do you want to use ways of handling their behaviour that make it more likely that they will learn to behave better next time.

Ideally you need to give children a chance to stop themselves. If they won't or really can't stop without your intervention, you want to act in line with your rules so that children feel you have been fair. As far as possible you need to deal with children in such a way that they don't feel they have been made to look silly in front of the others.

ACTIVITY

Think about one day's work with a group of children. Write down the name of each child and note against each name something you said or did to show that you were pleased with the child.

Discuss your notes with your supervisor. What differences do you notice between how you encourage individual children? Do you have a child on your list who behaves so badly that it's hard to be pleased about anything he or she does? Discuss what you could do.

When children have been given a chance and persist in misbehaving, you can impose a consequence that makes sense in the light of what they have done. For example:

● Two workers take a group of children to the local park. Amy, 4 years old, dashes off across the grass and is brought back. Two minutes later she dashes off in the opposite direction.

Amy is old enough to understand that she should stay close to workers on trips out. The workers can say something such as, 'Amy, since we can't trust you to behave like a big girl you will have to hold a hand like a little girl'. It will be important that the worker who holds Amy's hand is pleasant, although firm with her. The workers will have to give Amy chances to show she can be trusted on future trips – reminding her briefly of what they expect.

Ignoring

You don't have to take action – by word or deed – every time a child misbehaves. When you do take action it's sensible not to get any more cross than the situation really deserves.

Sometimes you may decide to ignore what a child is doing. This reaction makes sense if you judge that the misbehaviour isn't serious and the child is very likely to stop of her own accord. You need to watch carefully and probably move to the child with, 'Finished now? Come on – let's look at this'.

Some children do something that they know is not allowed in order to get your attention. Experience will tell you that 3-year-old Peter will soon stop kicking the toy box if you don't rise to the challenge but 4-year-old Marjorie will go on flicking sand until you say, 'That's enough!' and remove her from the sand tray. It's equally important that you go across to Peter when he has stopped and help him to become involved in an activity.

Catching and warning

If you keep alert to what is going on in a group then you can sometimes catch and divert children. You can give them a warning so they have a chance to pull back. For example, you can use the following:

● a warning look – a frown or shake of the head;
● warning words – perhaps that you will take away the bricks if Jon throws them one more time;
● tell a child firmly 'No' and offer an alternative activity as a distraction.

EXAMPLE

18-month-old Reuben is fascinated by the waving leaves of a plant. He has been told several times not to touch or rip the leaves but his hand keeps moving towards it. Note down two things that you think would be sensible to do with Reuben. Discuss with your supervisor.

When you can't divert them

Sometimes you won't be able to see something coming. Or else children persist because they want a reaction from you. You need to communicate that you're not pleased, but you don't have to be thoroughly unpleasant.

Children learn best if what you do is clearly linked with what they have done and the steps you take happen soon after they have misbehaved. Children who won't behave themselves should lose out as a consequence – for the moment. For example:

- You take Angela away from the home corner because she keeps grabbing all the cups and plates for herself. You settle her at the sticking activity where a worker is on hand to make sure she doesn't take all the materials.

- A worker brings two children out of the special story time because they wouldn't stop pinching each other. They have to help tidy up the book corner with another worker.

Children who misuse play materials are separated from them. Those who interrupt the enjoyment of other children may have to go and sit somewhere else. Of course you have to be realistic in your expectations – it's not reasonable to expect a 2-year-old to sit quietly for a 15-minute group story time. You can explain simply to a 3- or 4-year-old how she needs to behave if she wants to return to the home corner or have the book back.

Don't go on and on

You will help a child to behave better next time if this time you keep what you have to say brief and to the point. Make sure that the child is attending and say it once. Do what you need to do promptly since even 6- or 7-year-olds will have largely forgotten their misbehaviour if you don't react until the end of the day.

Once you have dealt with an incident then don't hark back to it later – either by what you say or by excluding a child from an afternoon activity when he has already 'paid' for his morning's misbehaviour. Children will feel resentful if they can't start again with a clean slate. It's also important that you stop other children teasing a child who has got into trouble. You might say something like, 'Don't go on at Gerry. He and I have worked it out. It's over now'.

A cooling off time

Children sometimes need to calm down and so may you. You need to handle any cooling off time with care:

- It's all right to tell a child to 'sit on that chair and be quiet for a while'. However, this 'while' must be very short – a couple of minutes at most. And you must return to the child swiftly – perhaps have a brief chat – and get him settled back into play. It's better not to have a regular place, like a naughty chair or a corner. Children feel singled out as a bad child.

Sometimes you need to hold children

The embarrassment, or anger at you, gets in the way of quietening down.

- You can't expect children younger than 3 years to stay still and calm down in this way. You need to talk quietly to them and even hold them if they can be comforted.

Children of 2 or 3 years in a ferocious tantrum may simply not listen to you. You may decide to put them safely on the floor to thrash and yell. You should stay close and be ready to comfort them as they emerge. You may need to hold them securely from behind if they seem likely to hurt themselves or other children.

Helping to put things right

Children might not voluntarily clear up a mess they have made or apologise to a child they have hurt. You may insist that they do put things right in this way although it's unlikely to be worth making an argument out of it. It's appropriate that you should then thank them when they have apologised or helped to tidy up.

Persuasion and compromise

You're an adult – not a child – but workers, who are honest, realise that they can slip into child-level arguments. You may realise that pride is becoming more important that the original issue, for you as well as for the child. You're tempted to shout louder or resort to your greater strength. The following may help to avoid power battles:

Don't argue

Take a deep breath or even walk away for a moment, if that is possible. Don't resort to yelling.

If you are clear about your rules then you will be more likely to avoid arguments with children over something that didn't matter that much. Some children enjoy an argument and get a lot of pleasure out of goading adults.

You have many more ideas than children. Use your imagination on ways to encourage children to do what you want:

- sometimes, friendly use of humour will jolly children along;
- a chase and a tickle may distract a toddler;
- a joke may defuse the situation with an older child but the humour must never be at the child's expense.

Give choices

If you insist that a child does one thing, such as he must tidy up all the bricks, then his only opportunity to assert himself is to refuse outright. You will get further and avoid a battle of wills if you offer a choice:

- perhaps he can tidy up the bricks or the books – then he feels as if he has a real say by opting for the books;
- perhaps he can tidy them up with your help;
- or you bet you can tidy up the books before he has finished the bricks.

Dislike a child's behaviour – not the child

Many people muddle up what children do with the person they are. You will hear it in the words that adults use – for example, 'She's such a spiteful child' or 'He's so stubborn'. When you label children like this, you sound as if you can see nothing but the child's misbehaviour. If you allow this habit to grow you will really find great difficulty in being positive about some children.

A child who hears herself labelled in this way will be very disheartened, and her parents will almost certainly argue with you rather than be ready to work together to change the child's behaviour.

You need to focus on what children are doing rather than depend on labels such as 'aggressive' or 'disruptive'. Until you are clear what the child is doing that disturbs you, you won't be able to adjust how you behave in order to change this child's behaviour. By all means dislike what children do sometimes and tell them that. You must also tell them that you like and value them.

EXAMPLE

5-year-old Julia has often been rude in rejecting another girl in the group. This week her remarks have included ridiculing the other child's hair and clothes. Julia is white, the other girl is Pakistani.

Note down what you could say to Julia about the incident. Think especially about how to communicate that you will not allow her to say things like this but you are not rejecting her as a person. Discuss your ideas with your supervisor and ask for advice on how best to support the second child.

ACTIVITY

You may find it hard to be positive about children who misbehave a great deal. Think about one child whose behaviour annoys you. Write down a description of what he or she does that you find so irritating.

Now write down at least three ways in which this child behaves well or takes positive advantage of what's on offer at the centre. Use your second list during the next week in order to praise this child. Think of yourself as catching this child out in good behaviour, not bad.

What about smacking?

You shouldn't smack children. It's against the law in state schools and will be against policy in centres.

A misuse of adult power

You are using your strength positively when you run to rescue a child who has wandered into the line of a swing. You will be able to catch and hold a child's arm or wrap your arms around a child's body to restrain children who are punching each other. However, adults who smack and shove children as a form of control are misusing their greater size and strength.

Teaching the wrong lesson

Children don't learn to behave differently when they are slapped. They feel cross at being humiliated or hurt from the pain. They learn not to let you see them doing whatever it was in the future.

Children who are smacked also learn to hit out in their turn because they feel someone has behaved badly, they are annoyed or just because they've had enough today.

Will I spoil them?

Children won't be spoiled by your putting more energy into encouraging what you do want than punishing what you don't. You won't spoil them by giving them compliments and thanking them for their efforts.

Children are spoiled by loads of rewards that bear little relationship to how they have behaved or by treats to keep them quiet rather than an adult's attention.

Children are also spoiled by being more favourably treated than other children for no good reason. They are spoiled if they are allowed to push other children away and dominate an adult's time or affection.

What about respect?

Some people confuse respect with the need for cold and hard discipline. Children don't learn to respect a worker who shouts at them or ridicules them in front of the group. They do learn to avoid that worker out of dislike or fear.

Insisting on very formal relations between workers and children doesn't ensure respect either. Children won't automatically respect an adult because of the difference in years or because they have to call you Mrs or Mr. If you exchange memories of school days with other workers, everyone will recall teachers whom they respected more than others.

Workers earn children's respect by behaving towards them in an honest and fair way, and this kind of behaviour sets a good example for children to follow.

Helping children learn how to behave

You will be able to help children to learn considerate ways of behaving and solving disputes as much as you encourage their language development or their physical skills. You will show them how to behave through your own example and by the way that you react when they misbehave.

Children, even very young ones, are far more likely to learn when your behaviour – words and actions – gives a clear message that you care about them. Children will realise that you notice and react warmly to their efforts to share toys or to solve a dispute by words rather than punching. They will also appreciate and behave better in your care as they realise that once you have dealt with an incident you forgive them and let them try again.

Continuing to learn

Different sources of learning

You'll benefit from the support of experienced workers who recognise what you can already do. As you gain more experience yourself, you'll become aware of the skills and information that you now need, or need to extend.

You will learn most effectively if you allow for the value of different sources of learning:

- from other adults – workers and parents – and from the children themselves, who can be very acute observers of behaviour if you invite their opinions;
- from written sources – books, practical material and specialist leaflets;
- from television documentaries and videos – yet another source of information and demonstration of ideas.

It's important that you remain open to new ideas and changes in advice in child care. You'll be an effective worker with babies and children if you value the skills and experience that you already have. However, you'll cease to be effective if you get complacent and believe you no longer need to learn.

Plan for your own personal learning

Gather your thoughts on how you would like to extend your learning in the future. Complete the following sentences to guide you:

I believe I already have skills in ...

I would like to improve my skills in ...

I would like to find out more about ...

In my work with the children, I think I need to improve in ...

In my contact with parents, I would like to be better at ...

I would like to have an opportunity to talk with someone who is experienced in ...

I would like to have a chance to visit a ...

I need to make contact with the following organisations to get advice or information ...

As you gain experience, you will be ready for our other book in this series, entitled *Caring for the under-8s – working to achieve good practice.*

Appendix 1: Links with the NVQs/SVQs

Level 2 core units	Sections of this book	Order of study	Facilities needed
C2: Care for children's physical needs	Chs 4, 7, 5.3, Ap 4		
C4: Support for children's social and emotional development	3.2, 5.2		
C6: Contribute to the management of children's behaviour	3.1, 3.2, Ch. 9		
C8: Set out and clear away play activities	Ch. 8		
C9: Work with young children	Chs 5, 8, 3.1, 3.2		
E1: Maintain a child oriented environment	Ch. 2		
E2: Maintain the safety of children	Chs 4, 6, 7		
P2: Establish and maintain relationships with parents of young children	3.3		
Level 2 Endorsement units			
C12: Feed babies	4.1, 6.2		
C13: Care for babies	Ch. 6, 3.2		
P9: Work with parents in a group for young children	3.4		

Appendix 2: Looking for more information and advice

As you work with different children and their families, you will find you need different kinds of information. Sometimes, you may be searching for definite advice on how best to help children and their families.

The following organisations operate in different ways. Many publish useful leaflets and some will offer general advice over the telephone. It is worthwhile writing or telephoning an organisation in order to find out what they offer and what, if any, charge they make for publications.

Please see this list as a beginning and add to it yourself. VOLCUF and the Early Childhood Unit (see addresses below) have compiled a national directory, *Organisations concerned with young children and their families*, 1992.

A. General information and resources for working with the under-8s

Afro-Caribbean Education Resource Centre (ACER)
ACER Centre, Wyvil Road, London SW8 2TJ (tel: 071–627–2662).

Comhairle Nan Sgoiltean Araich
(The Gaelic Pre-school Council), 21a Castle Street, Inverness IV2 3ER (tel: 0463–225469).

Early Childhood Unit
8 Wakley Street, London EC1V 7QE (tel: 071–278–9441).
The unit is part of the National Children's Bureau.

Kids' Club Network
279–281 Whitechapel Road, London E1 1BY (tel: 071–247–3009).
The network covers after school and holiday clubs for over-5s.

Plant yng Nghymru
(Children in Wales), 7 Cleeve House, Lambourne Crescent, Cardiff CF4 5GJ (tel: 0222–761177).

Playboard Northern Ireland
253 Lisburn Road, Belfast BT9 7EN (tel: 0232–382633).

Pre-school Playgroups Association
61–63 Kings Cross Road, London WC1X 9LL (tel: 071–833–0991).

Scottish Out of School Alliance
c/o Strathclyde After School Care Association, 39 Hope Street, Glasgow, G2 6AE (tel: 041–221–8119).

VOLCUF – Voluntary Organisations Liaison Council for the Under Fives
77 Holloway Road, London N7 8JZ (tel: 071–607–9573).

Working Group Against Racism in Children's Resources (WGARCR)
Lady Margaret Hall Settlement, 460 Wandsworth Road, London SW8 3LX
(tel: 071–627–4594).

B. Health and well-being of the under-8s

Always talk with the parents of children who are ill or who have a continuing condition that will affect their play or development. Material
from the following organisations could help you to build up a broader
understanding.

Action for Sick Children
Argyle House, 29–31 Euston Road, London NW1 2SD (tel: 071–833–2041).
An organisation concerned for children in hospital.

Association for Spina Bifida and Hydrocephalus
42 Park Road, Peterborough PE1 2UQ (tel: 0733–555988).

AVERT – the AIDS Education and Research Trust
11 Denne Parade, Horsham, West Sussex, RH12 1JD (tel: 0403–210202).

British Dyslexia Association
98 London Road, Reading RG1 5AU (tel: 0734–668271/2).

British Epilepsy Association
Anstey House, 40 Hanover Square, Leeds L53 1BE (tel: general 0532–
439393; advice 0345–089599).

Child Accident Prevention Trust
18–20 Farringdon Lane, London EC1R 3AU (tel: 071–608–3828).

Council for Disabled Children
8 Wakley Street, London EC1V 7QE (tel: 071–278–9441).

Down's Syndrome Association
155 Mitcham Road, London SW17 9PG (tel: 081–682–4001).

Enuresis Resource and Information Centre (ERIC)
65 St Michael's Hill, Bristol BS2 8DZ (tel: 0272–264920). ERIC is a
national centre offering information and advice to parents and professionals on the problem of bed wetting.

Foundation for the Study of Infant Deaths
35 Belgrave Square, London SW1X 8QB (tel: 071–235–0965; helpline
071–235–1721).

Kidscape
World Trade Centre, Europe House, London E1 9AA (tel: 071–488–2400).
Kidscape has a range of material on teaching children personal safety, on
abuse of children and on bullying.

National Asthma Campaign
300 Upper Street, London N1 2XX (tel: 071–226–2260).

National Deaf Children's Society
45 Hereford Road, London W2 5AH (tel: 071–229–9272).

National Eczema Society
Tavistock House North, Tavistock Square, London WC1H 9SR (tel: 071–
388–4097).

National Meningitis Trust
Fern House, Bath Road, Stroud, Glos. GL5 3TJ (tel: 0453–751738).

Royal National Institute for the Blind
224 Great Portland Street, London W1N 6AA (tel: 071–388–1266).

Sickle Cell Society
54 Station Road, Harlesden, London NW10 4BU (tel: 081–961–7795).

Spastics Society
12 Park Crescent, London W1N 4EQ (tel: 071–636–5020).

Further reading

Bee, Helen (1989), *The Developing Child*, 5th edition, Harper Collins.

Elliott, Claire (1992), *Childhood*, Channel Four Television.

Jeffree, Dorothy and Roy McConkey (1993). *Let Me Play*, Human Horizons Series, Souvenir Press. (Play for children with disabilities.)

Lansdown, Richard (1980), *More Than Sympathy – The Everyday Needs of Sick and Handicapped Children and their Families*, Tavistock.

Leach, Penelope, *The No Smacking Guide to Good Behaviour*, from EPOCH, 77 Holloway Road, London N7 8JZ.

Lindon, Jennie (1993), *Child Development from Birth to Eight*, National Children's Bureau.

Lindon, Jennie and Lance (1993), *Your Child from 5–11*, Positive Parenting Series, Hodder and Stoughton.

Lindon, Jennie and Lance (1993), *Caring for the under-8s – working to achieve good practice*, Macmillan.

Paley, Vivian Gussin (1984), *Boys and Girls – Superheroes in the Doll Corner*, University of Chicago Press.

Petrie, Pat (1989), *Communicating with Children and Adults*, Edward Arnold.

Starting Points Series from VOLCUF (address in Appendix 2):
- (1990), *No. 6 Child Abuse*.
- (1991), *No. 8 Keeping Children Healthy*.
- (1992), *No. 13 Young Children under Stress*.

Index